C000079321

Ultimate Activity Book for Kids

This edition published by Parragon in 2009
Parragon
Queen Street House
4 Queen Street
Bath BA1 1HE, UK

ISBN 978-1-4075-8084-5

Printed in Indonesia

Ultimate Activity Book for Kids

Bath · New York · Singapore · Hong Kong · Cologne · Delhi · Melbourne

Contents

PAPERCRAFT

RECYCLE IT!

FOOD FUN

GREAT GIFTS

MODELLING

TOYS and GAMES

SPECIAL OCCASIONS

NATURECRAFT

Measurements and recipes

Follow these recipes for perfect papier mâché and super salt dough. Use them for the projects in this book, or to create your own masterpieces!

Papier mâché

Papier mâché is brilliant for making all kinds of models. There are lots of different recipes, but this is the easiest.

You will need:

✦ Newspaper, torn into short strips.

✦ Dish of PVA glue, mixed with an equal amount of water (you can add a little wallpaper paste if you like).

✦ Old paintbrush.

Paste the strips of paper with glue on both sides, using a paintbrush. Place the strips one at a time over the object to be covered and smooth them down with your hands. Add one layer at a time – don't put too many on at once or it will take too long to dry.

You can make a bowl either by covering a balloon (*p128*) or wrapping layers round a real bowl. If you do this, smear petroleum jelly over the bowl before you start, so the model will slip off easily when it's dry.

Salt dough

This recipe will make enough salt dough for the basket on p140. You'll only need a quarter of the recipe to make sherriff's badges (p142).

You will need:

- ✦ 100g plain flour
- ✦ 50g salt
- ✦ 1 teaspoon cooking oil
- ✦ 80ml water
- ✦ Mixing bowl
- ✦ Board

Mix together the flour, salt and cooking oil in a bowl using your fingers. Add a little water and mix it in thoroughly until you have a smooth and thick dough which is dry enough not to stick to the sides of the bowl. If your mixture is too sticky, simply add more flour. If it's too crumbly, add water.

Sprinkle a little flour over the board and knead the dough on it until it is a smooth lump. You can store the dough in a sealed container in the fridge for a couple of days.

Bake in a pre-heated oven at 120°C for about three hours until firm. Baking times will vary depending on the size and thickness of your object, but make sure it's hard all through.

Oven temperatures

Gas mark	Centigrade	Fahrenheit
½	120	250
2	150	300
4	180	350
6	200	400
8	230	450

Get crafty!

Here's the low-down on the best materials to use, and ways to save your hard-earned pocket money by becoming a crafty collector.

Essentials

It's a good idea to keep all your craft materials together. You could design your own craft box from the project on p62.

Here's a useful list of the things you'll need to do most of the projects in this book. And don't forget – birthdays and Christmas are useful times to ask for that special set of paints you can't afford from your pocket money.

- ✦ A set of acrylic or poster paints and brushes
- ✦ Coloured pencils and felt-tipped pens
- ✦ A pot of PVA glue and an old brush
- ✦ Scissors – the ones with rounded ends are the safest
- ✦ Black fine-tipped fibre pen
- ✦ Pencil, ruler and a rubber

Materials

There are some things you have to buy, but you can recycle or go hunting for lots of stuff. See how good you can get at finding craft materials for free.

Saving paper

Don't eagerly tear the gift wrap off presents – a crafty collector saves wrapping paper. If it's very crumpled, get an adult to iron it with a cool iron, and it will be as good as new.

Cardboard

Cardboard comes in different thicknesses. Often, you can use recycled card instead of buying it, so save all your cereal and soap powder boxes. Flat-pack furniture often comes in corrugated card, so keep a look-out for it.

Fabric

Have you grown out of your favourite jeans? Don't worry, you can recycle them. Denim can be turned into bags, purses, pencil cases – the list is endless! Save scraps of patterned fabric too. They can be used to decorate your creations.

Bits and pieces

The crafty collector knows that buttons and beads make great decorations. You can make monster eyes from buttons and jewellery from beads. Even bottle tops come in handy!

Nature trail

When you're out and about, you'll come across all kinds of things to add to your store. Pick up leaves, twigs, feathers and seed heads in the park and collect flowers from the garden to dry (but ask first before you pick any prize blooms!)

Tips for success

Follow these simple rules and all your projects will be a rip-roaring success.

1. Protect from mess

If you're working on something messy, make sure you cover your workspace first with newpaper or a paper tablecloth. And don't wear your best trainers – wear clothes that you don't mind getting spattered.

2. Wash your hands

Nothing looks worse that a lovely hand-made card with a big, grubby thumbprint right in the middle of it! So make sure your hands are really clean before you start.

3. Be patient

Sometimes you have to leave paint, glue or clay to dry. No matter how keen you are to get on with your creation, it's worth waiting – your results will be so much better.

4. Use your ruler

If a project gives you measurements, make sure you measure as accurately as you can. Success might depend on it!

5. Follow the steps

Try to follow each step carefully. We've tested all the projects, and we know they work, and we want them to work for you too.

6. Tidy up

When you've finished, make sure you clean up any mess, gather up all your materials and store them together, ready for the next time you want to get creative.

PAPERCRAFT

PAPERCRAFT

Paper poppies

These poppies look very realistic, especially when light shines through the crêpe paper petals.

You Will Need

For each poppy:

- Crêpe paper in red, light green and dark green
- Scissors
- 2 pieces green garden wire
- 20 small black beads
- Black felt
- PVA glue and brush
- Zig-zag scissors

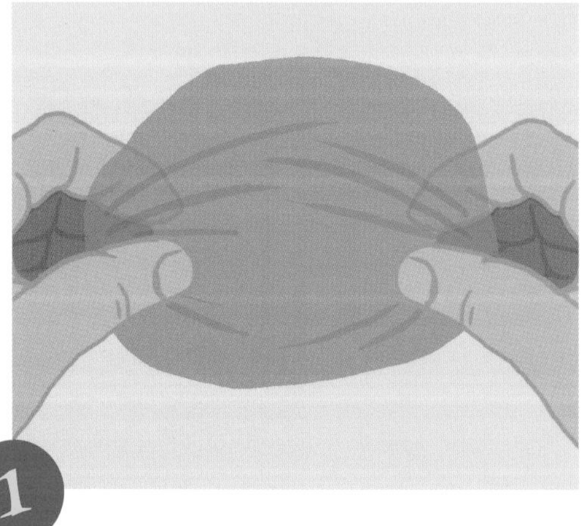

1

Cut out six circles from the red crêpe, about 70mm diameter. Pull gently on each circle to stretch them into a dish shape.

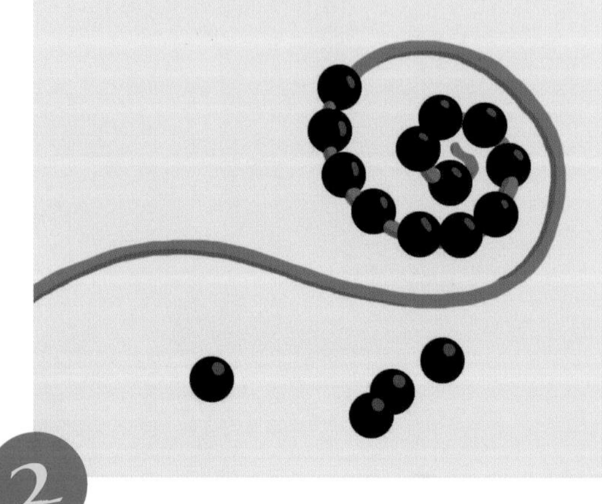

2

Twist the tip of the garden wire and thread 20 black beads onto it. Twist the beaded wire into a tight spiral shape.

◂ Using the zig-zag scissors, cut out a 4cm circle from the black felt. Stack the paper discs loosely on top of one another with the felt circle on top. Poke the non-beaded end of the wire through the centre and pull it through.

◂ Cut 1cm strips of dark green paper and paste them with PVA glue. Stick the top of the strip to the back of the flower and wind it all the way down the wire. Wrap a shorter piece of wire in the same way.

Twist the two pieces of wire together to make a stem and leaf. Using the zig-zag scissors, cut a leaf shape from the light green crêpe and glue it to the underside of the leaf stem.

Posy of pansies

Make these pansies in the same way, using lilac crêpe paper. Cut a figure-of-eight from the black felt and thread the wire with a single yellow bead to make the flowers' centres.

Cut-out supermodel

Do you fancy yourself as a fashion designer? Get creative and make a catwalk collection for your very own supermodel.

You Will Need

- Fashion magazine
- Tracing paper
- Pencil
- Coloured pencils
- Scissors
- A4 sheet of thin white card
- Thick white paper
- 2 cocktail sticks
- Sticky tape
- Blob of self-hardening clay

1

Choose a photo of a model from a magazine. Trace the outline of her body.

2

Remove the tracing paper and transfer the outline onto thin white card and, as shown above, cut it out.

◂ Use coloured pencils to draw a slip on your model and colour her skin and hair. Draw a face. Carefully draw a thin black outline round her.

3

4

Put the model on a sheet of paper and draw lightly round her, so that you know the right size for her clothes. Make different outfits and matching accessories such as shoes and bags. Add tags to the clothes so that you will be able to attach them to your model.

5

Make a box-shaped stand out of self-hardening clay. Poke two holes in the clay with the cocktail sticks and leave to dry. Tape a cocktail stick to the back of each leg, leaving about 1.5cm at the bottom. Insert the sticks into the holes on the stand.

PAPERCRAFT

Dinosaur letter rack

An armour-plated stegosaurus is just what you need to keep your important cards and letters from escaping!

1

Trace the templates on p221 onto purple card. Cut out two dinosaur shapes and two bases. Trace the face and neck onto one of the dinosaur shapes.

You Will Need

- 2 sheets thick A4 purple card
- Tracing paper
- Pencil
- Scissors
- Sheet of orange paper
- PVA glue
- 2 stick-on googly eyes
- Stick-on yellow spots
- Black felt-tipped pen

2

Trace the armour plates onto orange paper. Cut them out, making them a little smaller than your outline. Glue them, one at a time, along the spine of the dinosaur, leaving a border round each shape.

3

Glue on the googly eyes and go over the face and mouth with a black felt-tipped pen.

4

Cover the body shapes with yellow stick-on dots.

5

Cut out four legs in each dinosaur shape. Cut two slots in the base shapes. Slot the shapes together so that you make a letter holder.

PAPERCRAFT

Mini gift box

This box is great for home-made sweets, such as the peppermint creams on p68. Wrap them in greaseproof paper and pop them in. Brilliant!

You Will Need

- Thick paper 40 x 30cm
- Acrylic paints: blue, green
- Paintbrush
- Ruler
- Scissors
- PVA glue
- Small piece of ribbon
- Hole punch

1 Brush clean water over the paper. While the paper is damp, paint on blue and green stripes – the colours will run and make blurry stripes. Leave to dry.

2 Fold the paper in half and make a sharp crease. Unfold the paper again.

3 Fold the sides in so that they meet in the middle, where you made the crease. Make sharp creases, then unfold the paper.

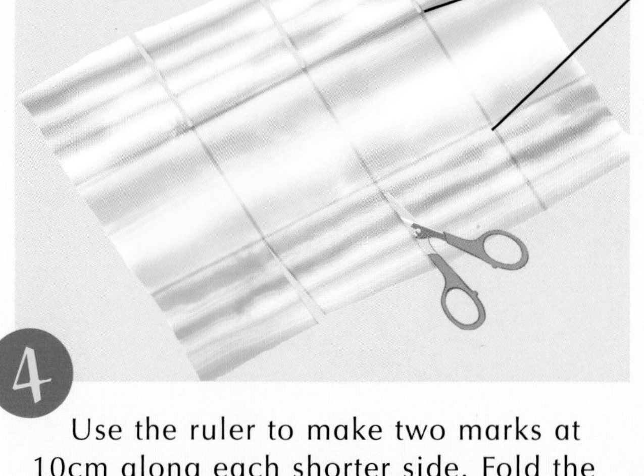

4

Use the ruler to make two marks at 10cm along each shorter side. Fold the paper at the marks, then unfold. You will have a grid of folds across the paper. Cut three slits along the top and three at the bottom.

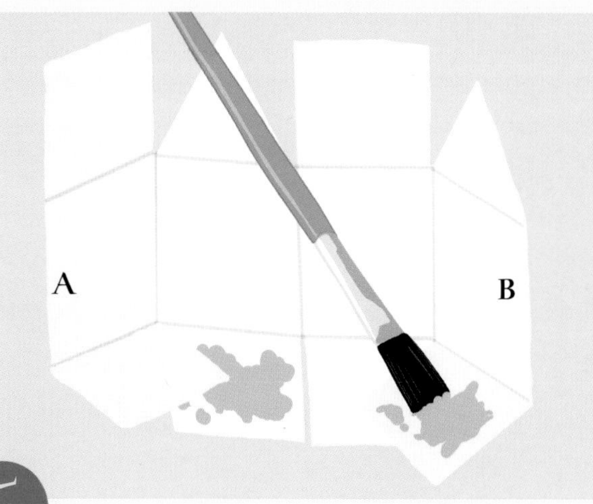

5

Snip the 2nd and 4th tabs along the top into points. Now shape the whole sheet into a box by bringing the edges A and B together. Glue the bottom pieces together where they overlap.

6

Use a hole punch to make a hole in each pointed tab. Thread ribbon through the holes and tie in a bow.

Piggy bookmark

When you're under orders to put down your favourite book and turn out the lights, this piggy bookmark will help you keep your place!

You Will Need

- Strip of card or thick paper 4cm x 21cm
- Scrap of pink card or thick paper 7cm square
- Pencil
- Scissors
- PVA glue
- 2 stick-on googly eyes
- Black felt-tipped pen

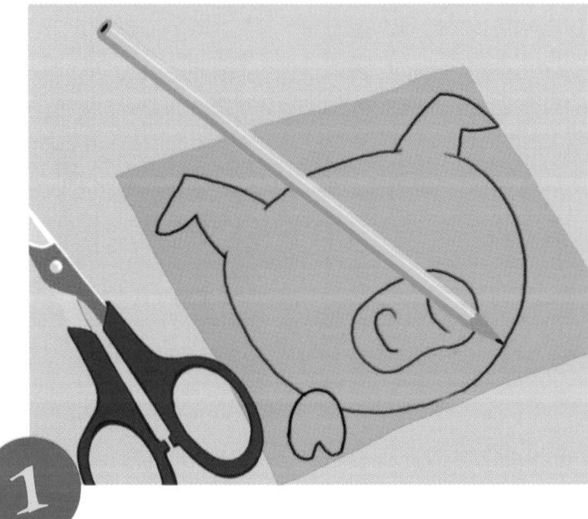

1 Draw the outline of a pig's face and two trotters on the pink card. Cut the pig shape out.

2 Stick on the googly eyes using the PVA glue.

3

Using the black pen, draw round the nose and mouth, then add nostrils and ear creases. Colour the trotters black.

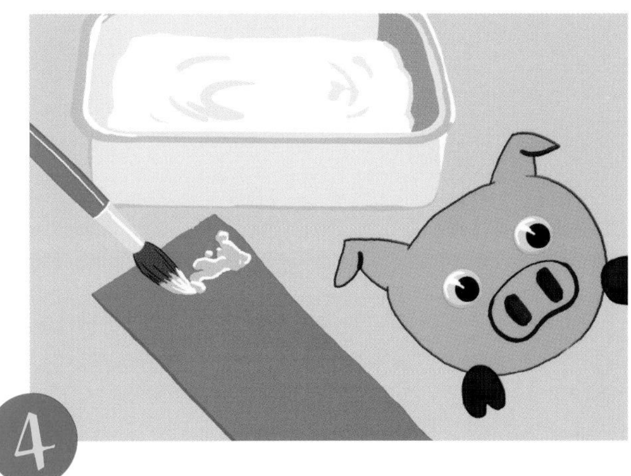

4

Glue the pig face to the strip of card. Make the head stick up about 2cm over the top of the strip. Leave it to dry.

Give your bookmarks a fluffy finishing touch by glueing a few threads of wool to the finished faces.

Try This!

Animal Farm

Make a colourful collection of animal bookmarks for all your favourite books. It's a great way to use up leftover strips of card from other projects. Try a pony, a cute cat, a dog or even a penguin.

Ballerina card

This dancer really comes alive when you open the card and her tutu pops out!

You Will Need

- White card 210mm square
- Pencil
- Set of coloured pencils
- Blue paper 297 x 160mm
- Scissors
- PVA glue

1

Fold the card in half. Draw a ballet dancer, in leotard and tights, in the middle of the card.

2

Colour in the ballerina using the colouring pencils.

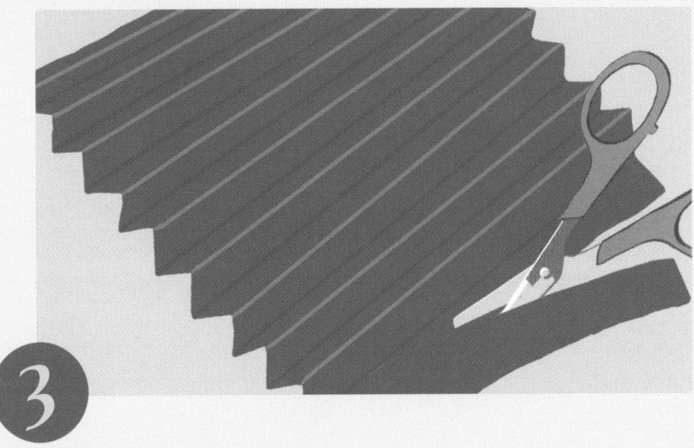

3

◂ Make folds along the shorter side of the blue paper about 1cm apart. Trim off any excess when you have folded almost to the end.

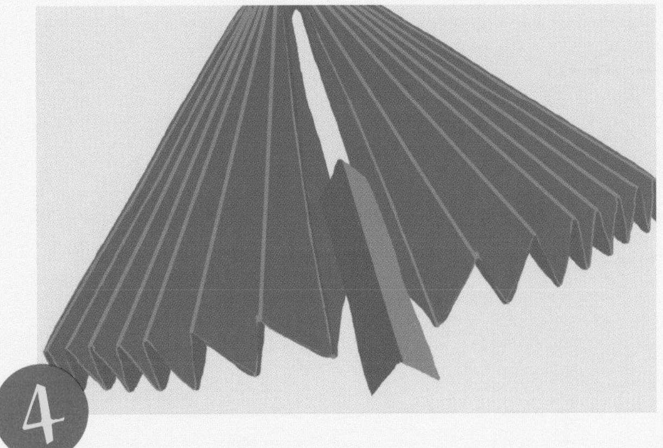

4

Fold the paper in half with the two shorter edges together. Cut a small piece of blue paper, fold it in half and glue it where the two ends meet, making a fan shape.

5

Glue along the edge of the fan. Put the fold in the middle of the card at the dancer's waist and stick the two edges down. Fold the card closed – when you open it, a tutu will pop up!

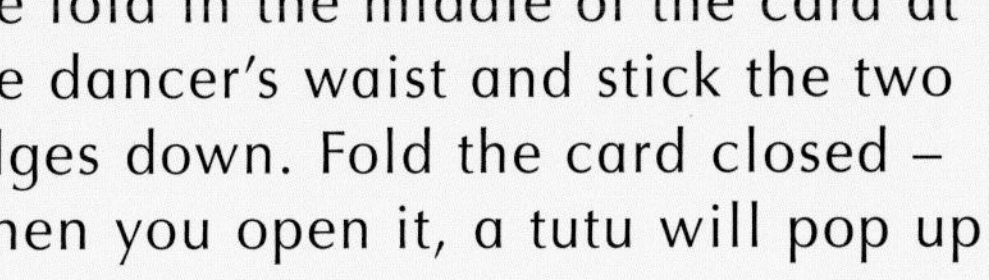

PAPERCRAFT

Bubble-print gift wrap

Don't waste your pocket money buying wrapping paper – make bubbly gift wrap instead. All you need is washing up liquid, paints and plenty of puff!

You Will Need

- Old newspapers
- Ready mixed paints: red, blue
- Washing-up liquid
- Water
- Old spoon
- Drinking straws
- Shallow bowl
- White paper

1

Cover the work surface with newspaper sheets; this is a messy project! Using an old spoon, stir together ½ cup water, 1-2 tablespoons red paint, and ½ tablespoon washing-up liquid in the bowl.

2

Put a straw in the paint mixture and gently blow to make bubbles. Keep blowing until the bubbles are almost over the edge of the dish.

3

Put a piece of paper on top of the bubbles and hold it there until several bubbles have popped. Move the paper and continue popping bubbles.

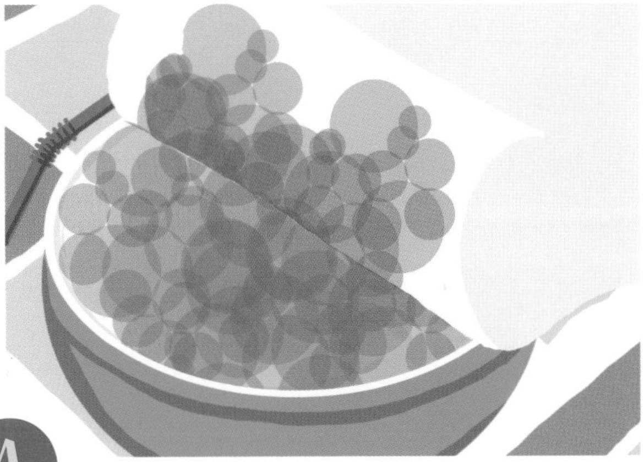

4

Clean the bowl and make a blue paint mixture. Repeat steps 1 to 3 so you have a blue and red bubbly pattern. Leave the paper to dry.

Top Tip

If you don't get enough bubbles when you blow, add a drop more washing up liquid. If the bubbles are too faint on the paper, add more paint to the mixture.

Printed star card

Why not make your own stamps and have a go at designing cards? All you need is paint, funky foam and some thick card.

You Will Need

- Sheet of blue card 300 x 150mm, folded in half
- Tracing paper and pencil
- 3 pieces funky foam 50 x 50mm
- 3 pieces thick card 50 x 50mm
- Scissors
- Poster paints: red, yellow, dark blue and brush
- PVA glue
- Red glitter

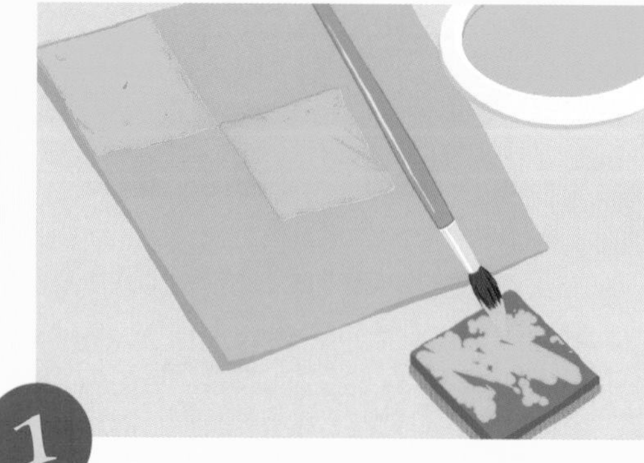

1 Stick a foam square onto a square of card. Add yellow paint to your stamp and print it in one corner of the card. Print four more squares in the corners and middle of the card. Leave to dry.

2 Meanwhile, trace a star, using the template on p220. Transfer it onto the foam and cut out two stars. Stick each star to squares of thick card.

3 Add blue paint to one of the star stamps and print a star onto each blue square, pressing down firmly.

4

Use the other star stamp to print red stars on the yellow squares. Leave the card to dry.

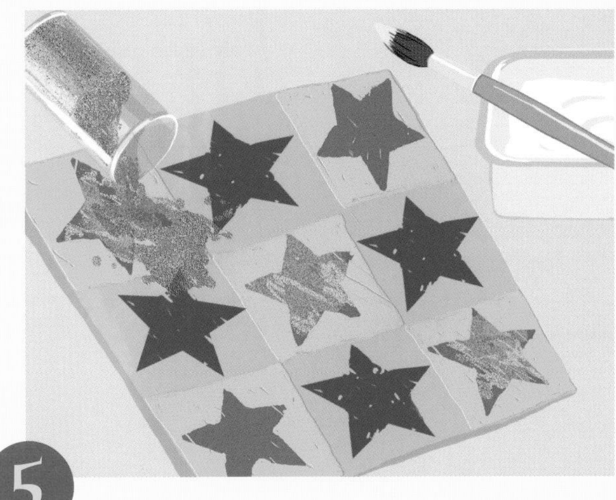

5

Dilute a little PVA glue with water and brush it onto the middle, top left and bottom right red stars. Sprinkle red glitter over the glued stars and shake off the excess glitter. Leave to dry.

Try This!

Gift tag

Make a matching gift tag by folding a piece of card 100 x 50mm in half and stamping each side. Finish by making a hole and threading through some red ribbon.

PAPERCRAFT

Groovy gift bag

If you have a gift that's an awkward shape and hard to wrap neatly, why not make a fab gift bag for it instead? It's really simple!

1

Brush glue on the white paper and stick the tissue paper to it. Then glue the wrapping paper to the other side of the white paper. Cut the glued sheets to 45 x 30cm.

You Will Need

- A3 sheet orange tissue paper
- 1 sheet patterned gift wrap
- A3 sheet of white paper
- Ruler and pencil
- PVA glue and brush
- ½ metre red ribbon, 2cm wide
- 25cm pink ribbon, 1cm wide

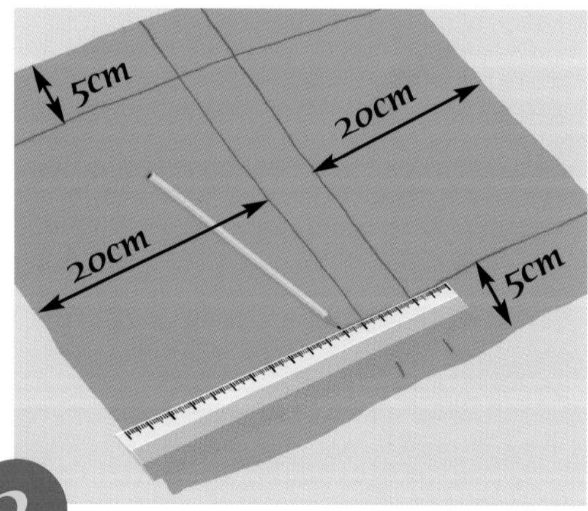

2

Draw two lines, 5cm from the top and bottom of the sheet. Then draw two lines 20cm in from the sides. Fold and unfold along the lines to make creases.

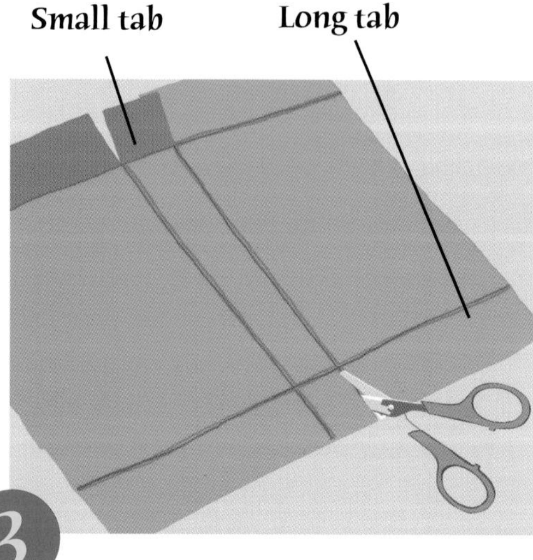

3

Use scissors to cut four slits up to where the lines cross, to make small and long tabs. Fold the two small tabs in.

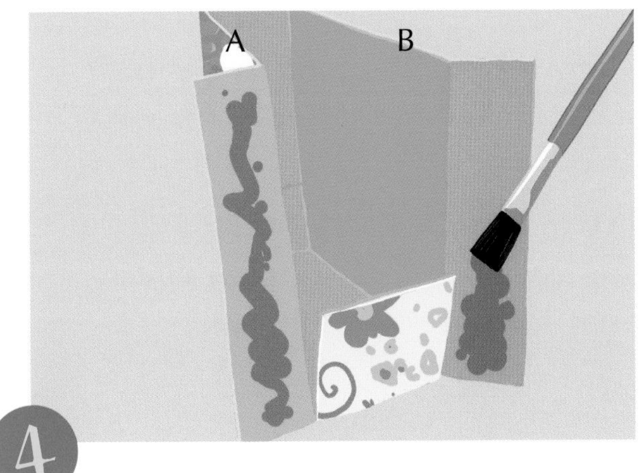

4

◂ This part is easier than it sounds! Paste glue along the four long tabs. Lift up the paper until edges A and B meet. Press the long tabs together then reach inside and pull up the small tags, glueing them to the sides. You wll now have a box shape.

5

Push the sides of the box together and make creases, so it looks like a bag. Make three holes along each side of the top of the bag. Thread orange ribbon through the outside holes on each side for handles. Make sure you knot the ribbon on the inside.

6

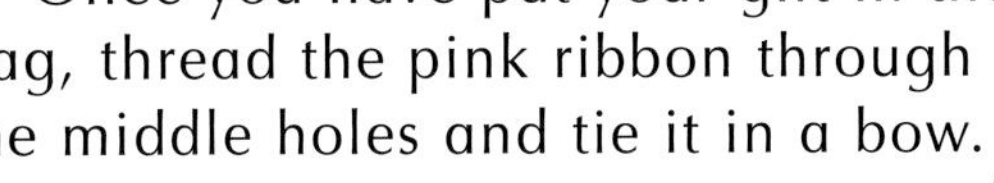

Once you have put your gift in the bag, thread the pink ribbon through the middle holes and tie it in a bow.

Paper aeroplanes

These simple paper gliders have a cunning secret to make them fly brilliantly. With a bit of practice, you can even make them loop through the air!

You Will Need

- Square sheet of coloured paper 210 x 210mm
- Stapler and staples
- Round stickers

1

Fold the sheet of paper in half. Turn down the corners at one end so that the turned down edges line up along your fold.

2

To make the wings, fold the top down again, lining it up along the bottom of the shape. Repeat on the other side.

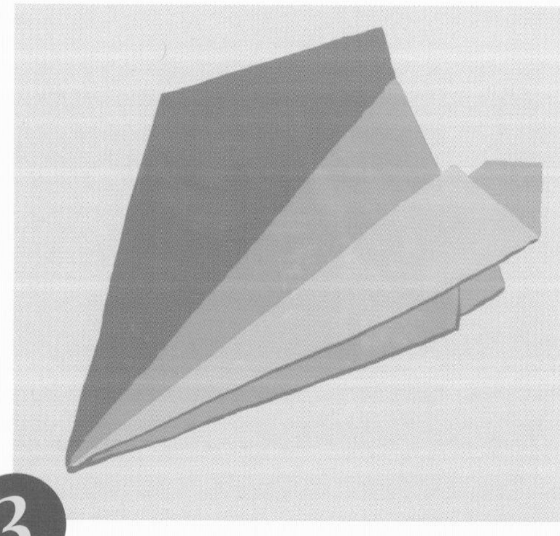

3

Fold the top flaps down again, lining them up along the bottom of the aeroplane.

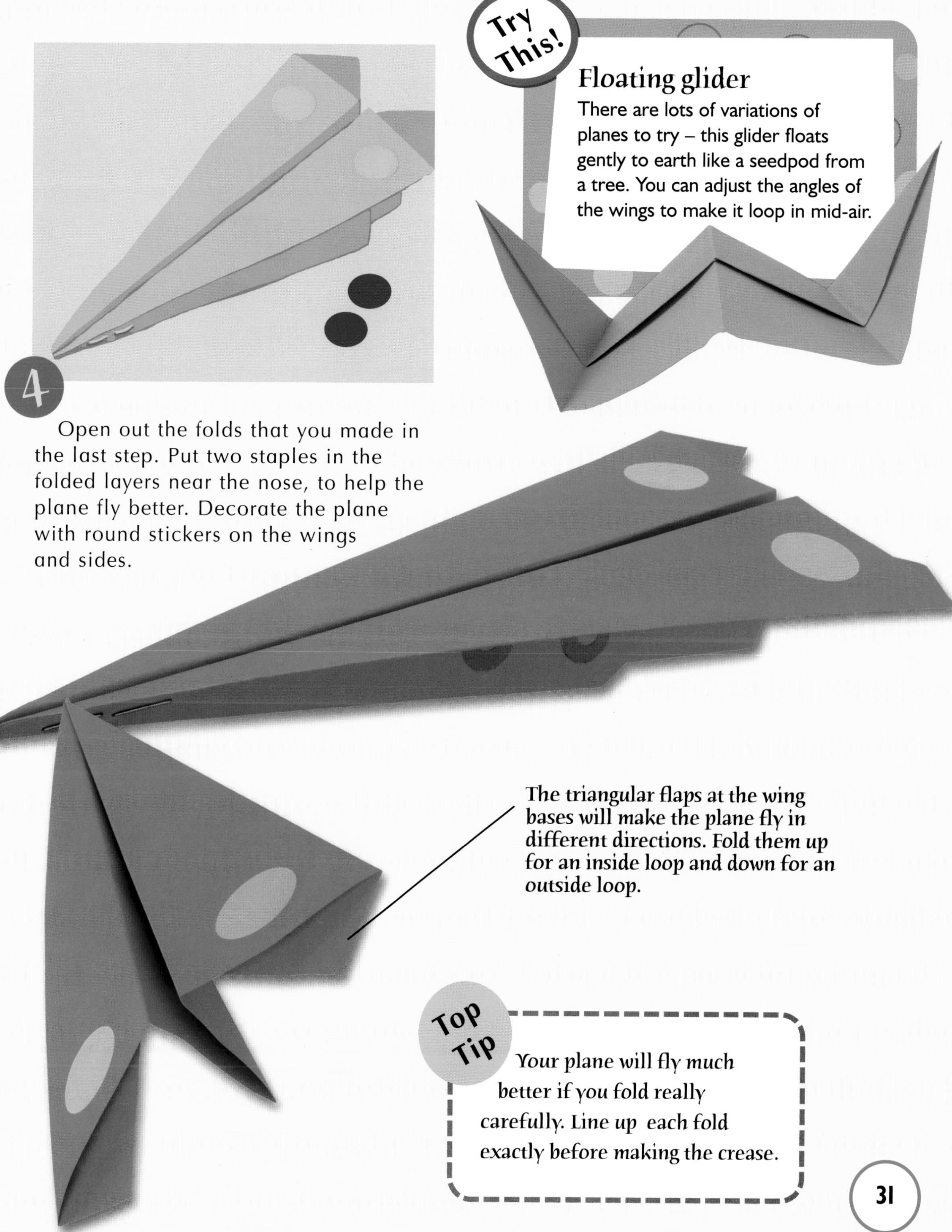

Floating glider

There are lots of variations of planes to try – this glider floats gently to earth like a seedpod from a tree. You can adjust the angles of the wings to make it loop in mid-air.

Open out the folds that you made in the last step. Put two staples in the folded layers near the nose, to help the plane fly better. Decorate the plane with round stickers on the wings and sides.

The triangular flaps at the wing bases will make the plane fly in different directions. Fold them up for an inside loop and down for an outside loop.

Top Tip

Your plane will fly much better if you fold really carefully. Line up each fold exactly before making the crease.

Card-players' gift wrap

Give gifts a playing-card theme by stencilling the shapes of the four suits onto tissue wrapping paper.

You Will Need

- 4 scraps of card, 6cm square
- Pencil
- Scissors
- Tissue paper
- Gold paint
- Saucer
- Piece of sponge (eg. washing-up sponge)
- Hole punch
- Thin gold ribbon

1 Fold each piece of card in half. Draw a half shape of a club, spade, heart and diamond against the fold. Cut them out and put the shapes to one side.

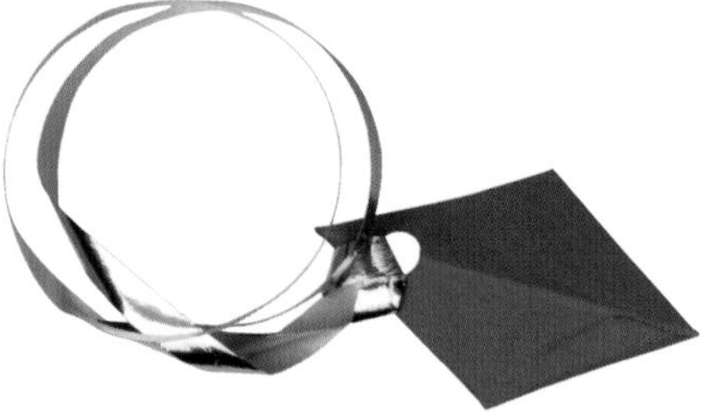

2 Put the gold paint in a saucer and dab the sponge lightly in it. Put the card with the spade-shaped hole onto the paper and hold it down with one hand while you dab the sponge over the hole. Remove the card when the paint is dry.

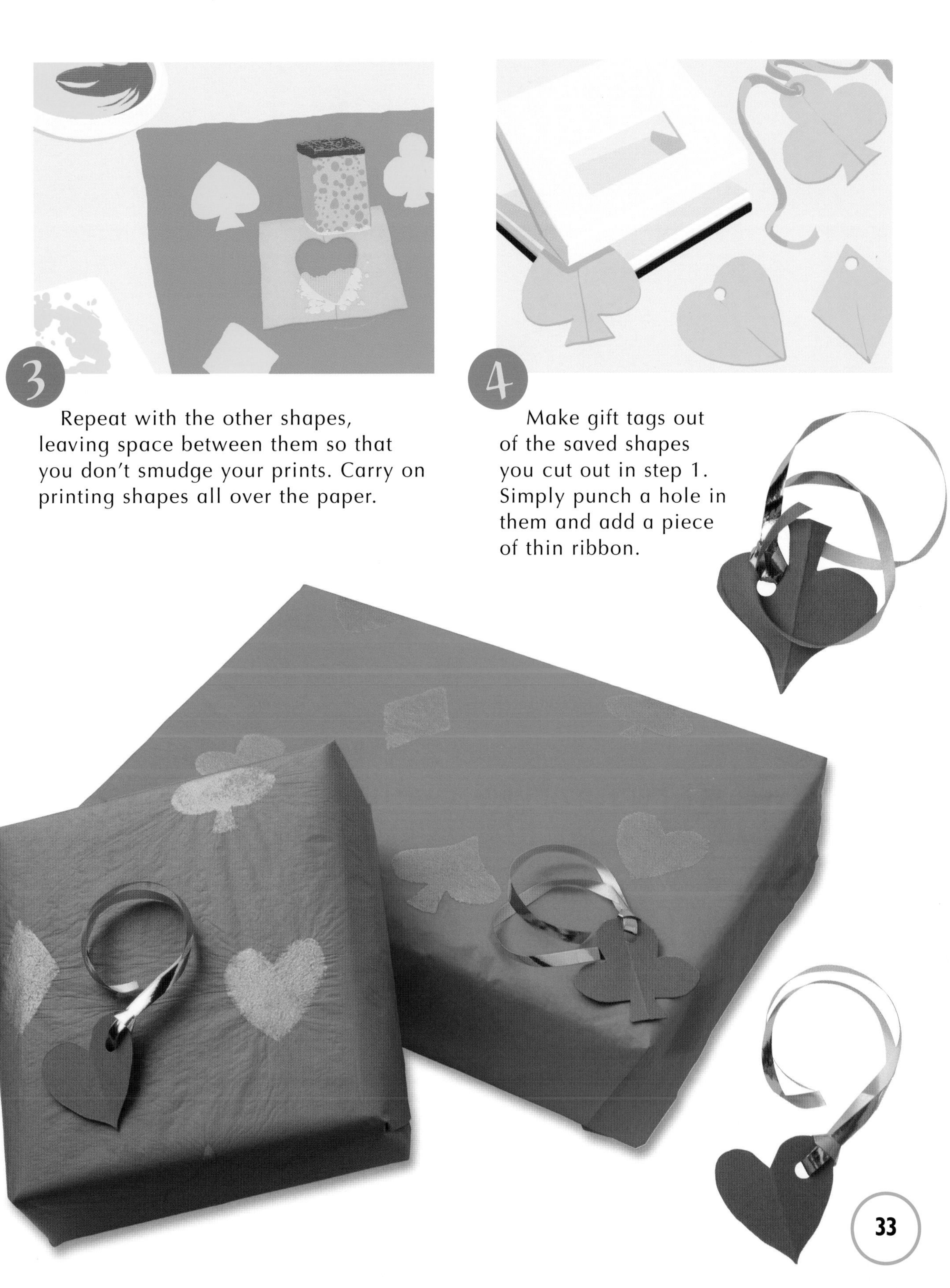

3

Repeat with the other shapes, leaving space between them so that you don't smudge your prints. Carry on printing shapes all over the paper.

4

Make gift tags out of the saved shapes you cut out in step 1. Simply punch a hole in them and add a piece of thin ribbon.

Donkey peg

Make a useful carrot-munching donkey peg to use on a clipboard or just to decorate your bedroom.

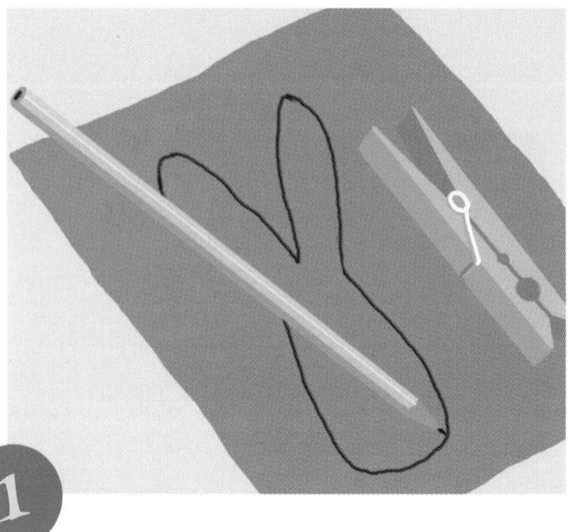

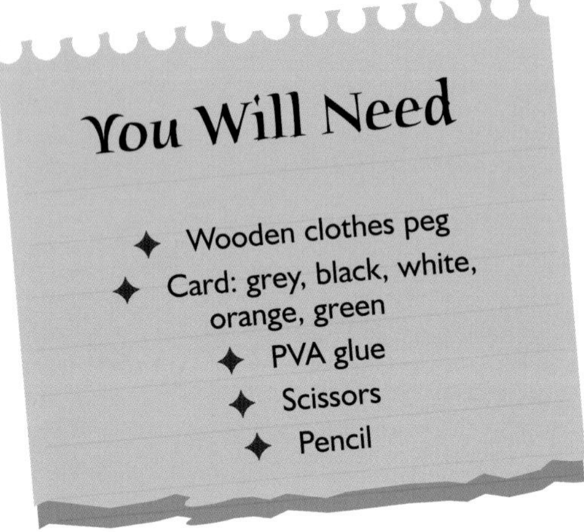

1

Draw the outline of a donkey's face onto grey card. Make the face a little longer than the clothes peg.

2

Now draw shapes onto coloured card: white circles for eyes, black pupils, eyebrows, mane and nostrils, an orange carrot and a green carrot stalk. Cut out all the shapes.

3

Glue all the features onto the donkey's face.

4

Paste a spot of glue on the back of the donkey, in the middle, and stick him to your peg. Leave it to dry.

Try This!

Cute cow

You can make all kinds of animal shapes to decorate pegs. Try a cow made from black, white and brown card, and make a tasty daisy for her to munch.

Tissue paper card

It's much more special to make cards than to buy them. Tear up some tissue paper and send a heart-felt message to somebody you really like!

1 Fold the card in half and run your finger firmly along the crease. Make sure your hands are really clean first.

You Will Need

- A4 sheet of white card
- Tissue paper: red, pink, blue
- PVA glue mixed with equal amount of water
- Pencil

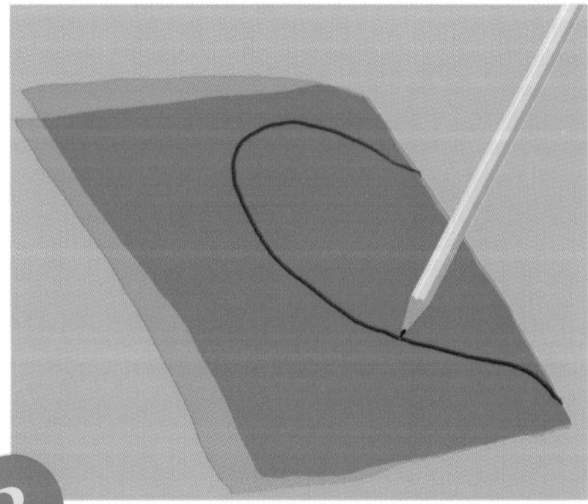

2 Fold the red tissue paper in half and lightly draw half a heart shape next to the fold.

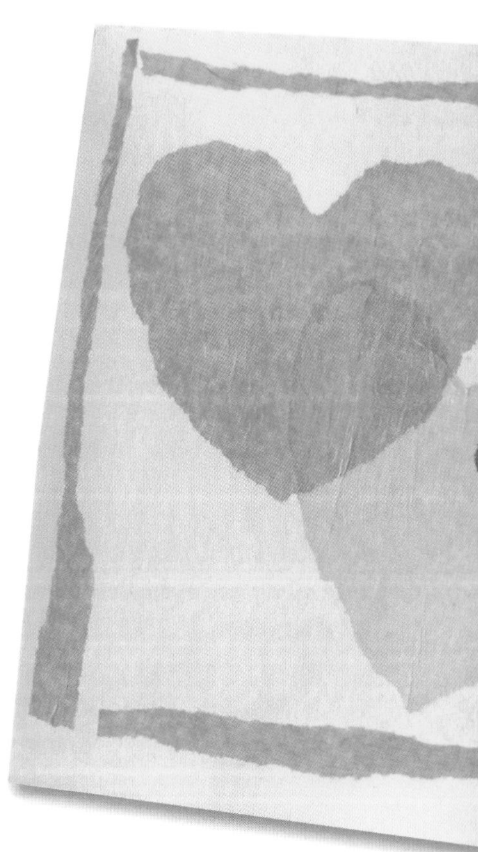

3

Tear the heart shape out of the tissue paper. Make different sized hearts in the same way from the other sheets of tissue. Don't worry if they look wonky – they're meant to!

Top Tip

If it's too fiddly to put glue onto the hearts, brush a really thin layer of glue mixture over the whole card, stick the hearts down, then leave the card to dry.

4

Carefully brush the glue onto the hearts and stick them onto the card. Make the shapes overlap each other.

5

Roughly tear thin strips from the leftover tissue and stick them round the edges of card to make a border.

PAPERCRAFT

Paper pompoms

Make your presents look really special with paper pompom decorations. Get some brightly coloured tissue paper and you'll soon be going pompom crazy!

You Will Need

- Tissue paper sheets in different shades
- PVA glue and brush

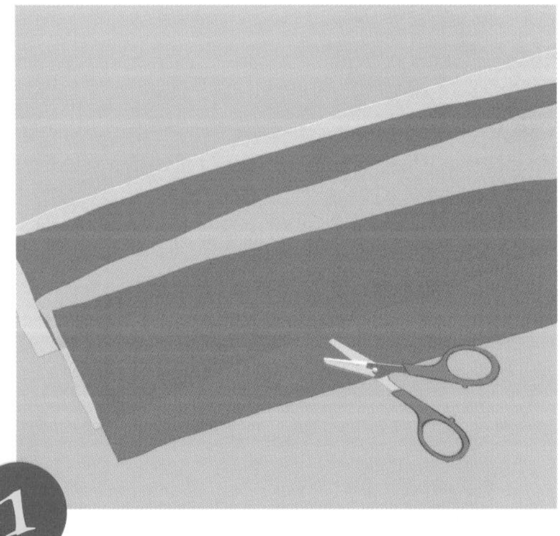

1 Cut two strips, 40x12cm, from each sheet of tissue paper.

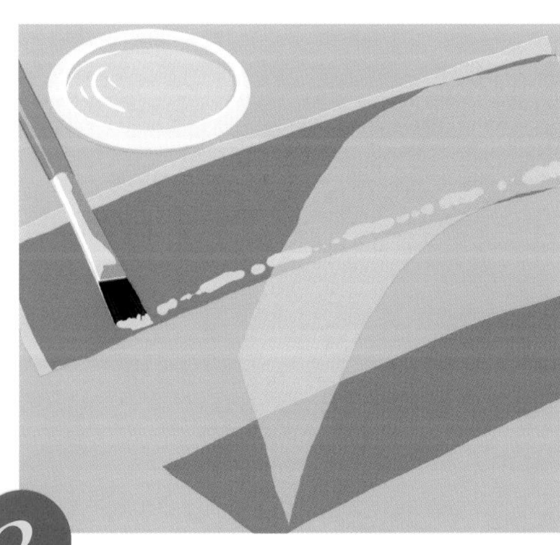

2 Brush glue along the bottom edge of each strip and stick all four strips together.

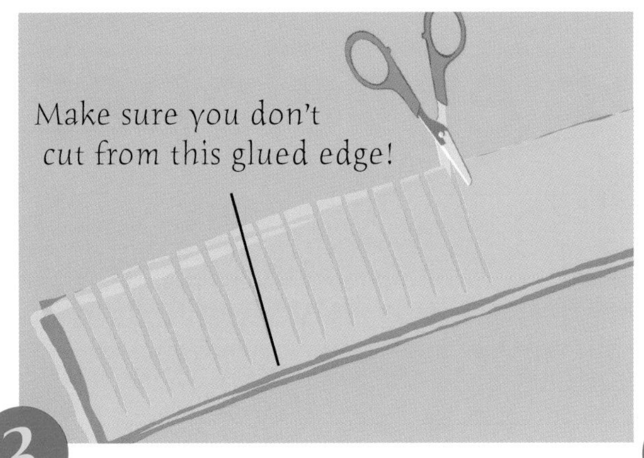

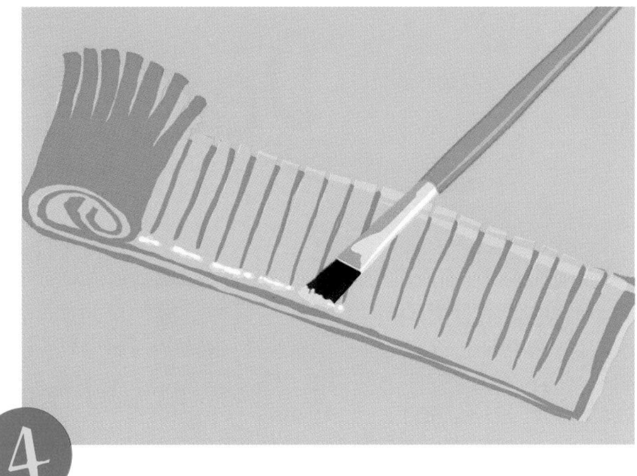

3

Use scissors to snip along the strips, making each cut about 1.5cm apart.

4

Spread glue along the bottom of the strip and roll the shape up. Press it together at the bottom and leave to dry.

Foil pompom

Decorate a special gift with a pompom made from shimmery foil paper. Use zig-zag scissors for a spiky look.

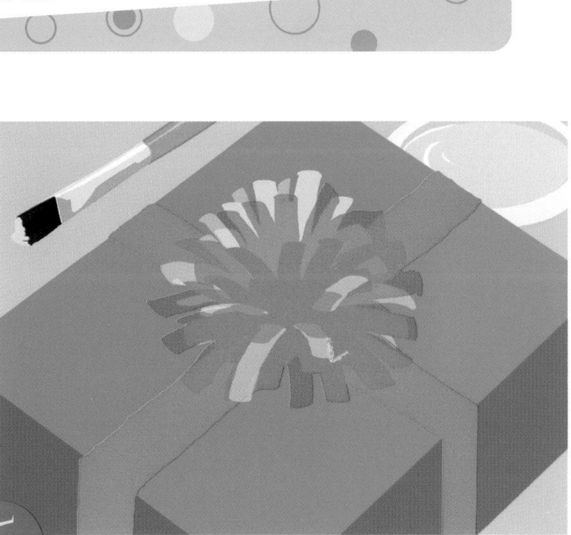

5

Use your fingers to fluff out the pompom. Dab some glue on the bottom and stick on a present.

Designer envelopes

If you enjoy making your own cards, why not design your own matching envelopes too? It's a great way to use up old gift wrap.

You Will Need

- Sheet of coloured A4 paper
- Patterned gift wrap
- Stick of glue
- Home-made card

1

Put your home-made card on the sheet of paper and fold the paper in on two sides and the bottom. Then fold over the top of the paper to make the flap.

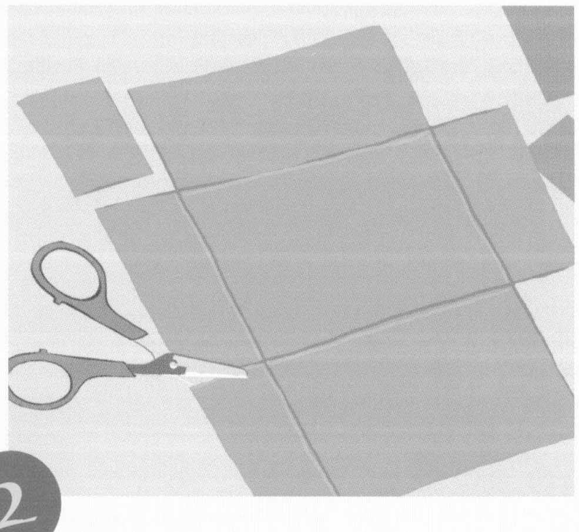

2

Unfold the paper and snip off the four small corner rectangle.

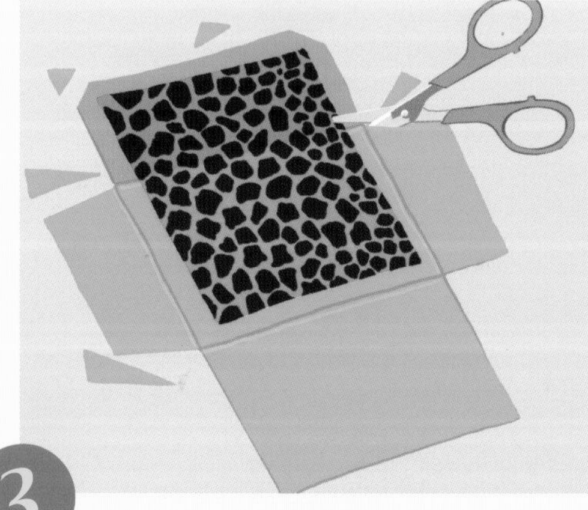

3

Cut a piece of patterned gift wrap to fit in the top flap and main area. Glue it in place. Trim off the corners of the top and side flaps.

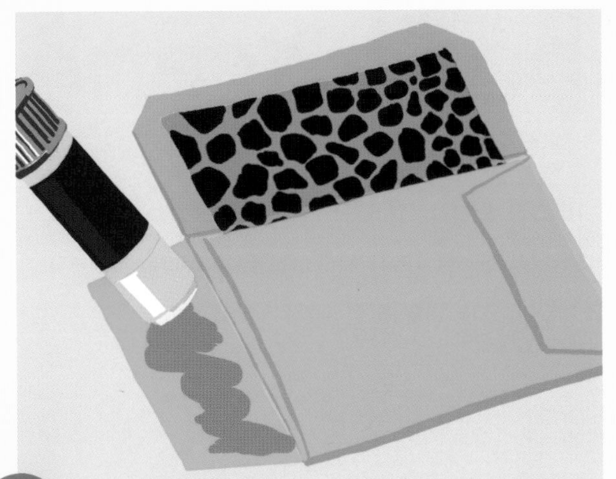

4

Fold up the bottom flap, then fold in the sides and glue them in place. Put in the card, then fold down and glue the top flap.

Try This!

Be creative!

Make a colourful envelope from patterned paper and stick on an address label. You can easily make your own labels on a computer.

Top Tip

If your card is small, you'll get a neater effect if you trim the paper all round the card after finishing step 1.

Add colourful stickers to decorate your envelope.

PAPERCRAFT

Mosaic boat scene

Do you fancy a change from painting your favourite pictures? Stick coloured scraps of paper onto your drawing instead, for a colourful mosaic effect.

1

Choose coloured sections of old magazines. Tear out scraps of green and blue for the sea and sky, bright shades for the sails and dark shades for the boats.

You Will Need

- Old magazines
- Scissors
- A4 sheet of white paper and pencil
- PVA glue
- Brush

2

Cut the scraps into squares of roughly the same size, about 1cm square.

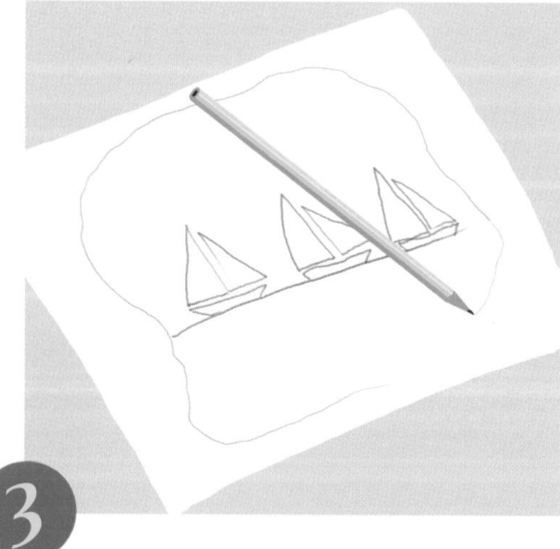

3

Lightly draw a seaside scene on the white paper. Draw a wavy line round the picture, as a guide to where to finish sticking squares.

4

Start placing the squares onto your picture. When you are happy with the design, glue the squares down.

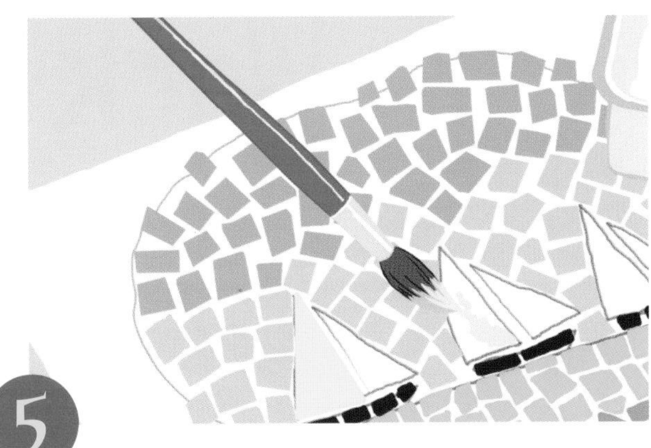

5

Make triangles to fit roughly into the sail shapes. Cut round the picture, then glue it to a larger square of blue paper.

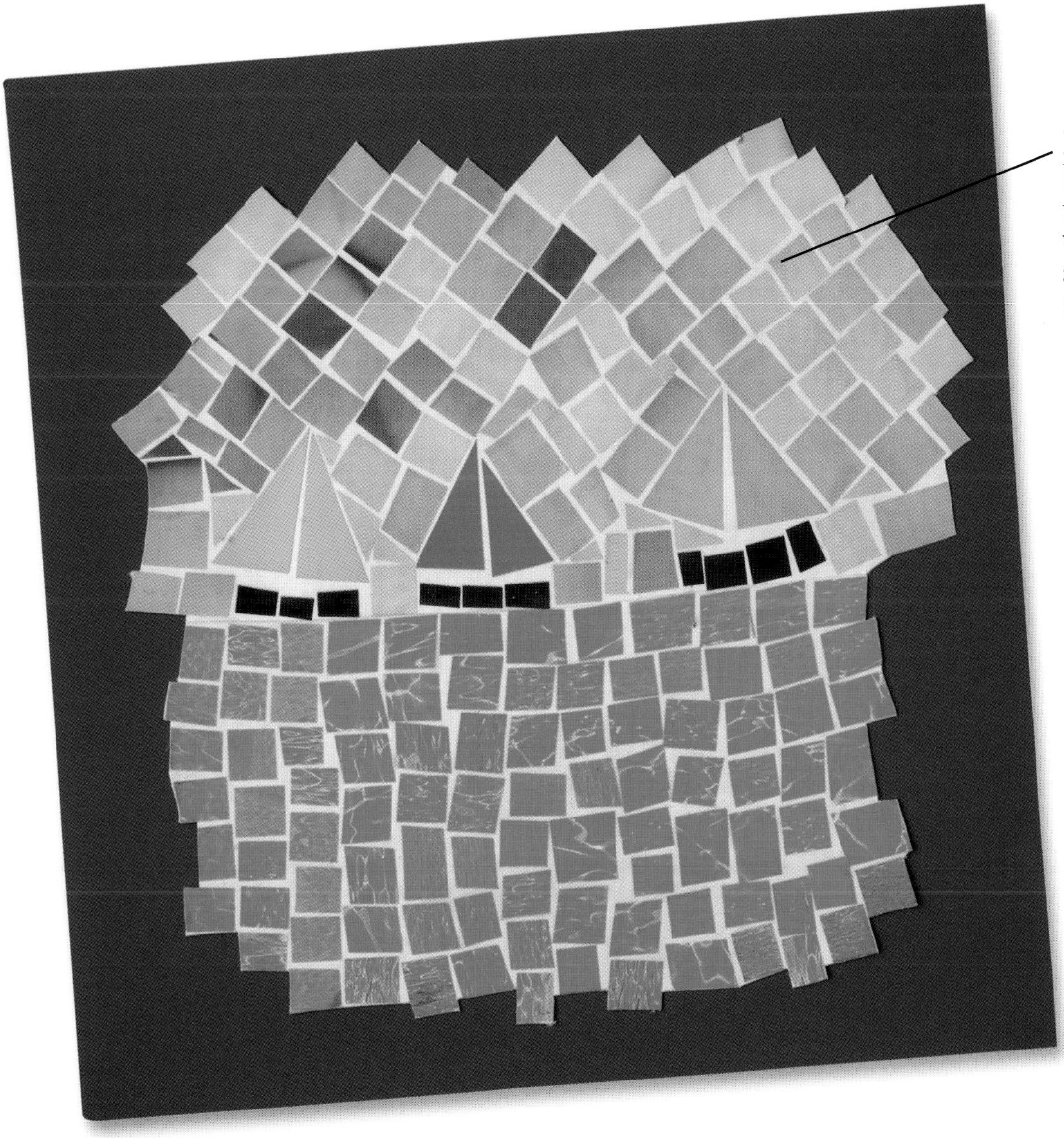

Leave space between the squares when you stick them down.

Wacky waste bin

Cheer up a boring bin by covering it in gift wrap to match your bedroom's colour scheme. You've got no excuse for an untidy room now!

You Will Need

- Round cardboard waste bin
- Roll of gift wrap
- Scissors
- PVA glue diluted with an equal amount of water
- Brush

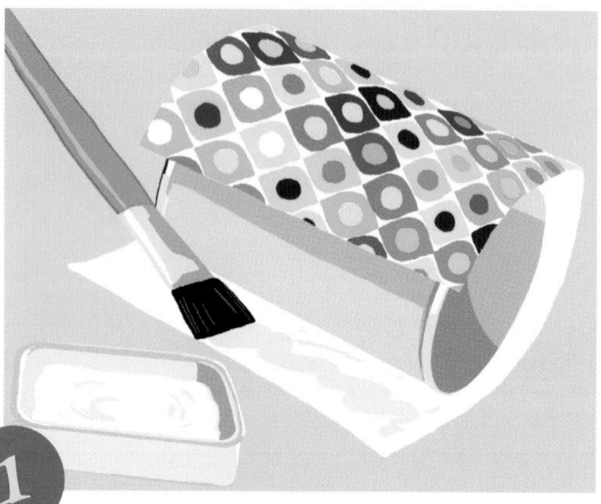

1. Cut a sheet of gift wrap long enough to fit round the bin, and 2cm wider than the bin at both ends. Wrap the paper round the bin and glue it in place.

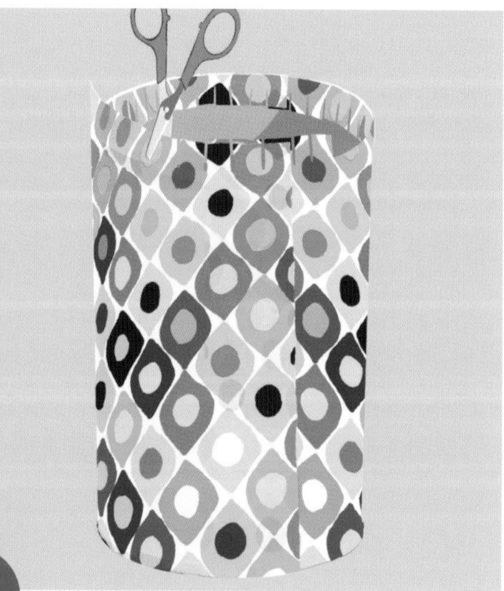

2. Make small snips in the top and bottom edges, fold them over neatly and glue them down.

RECYCLE IT!

RECYCLE IT!

Bird feeder

Hang this brilliant feeder in the garden and you'll soon have flocks of peckish birds calling in for a snack!

You Will Need

- Empty, rinsed-out juice carton
- Sandpaper
- Scissors
- Acrylic paints: dark brown, light brown, black, white, dark green, light green
- Paintbrush
- Bag of bird seed
- Garden wire

1 Roughen the outside of the carton with sandpaper. Cut out a long window on the side opposite the nozzle.

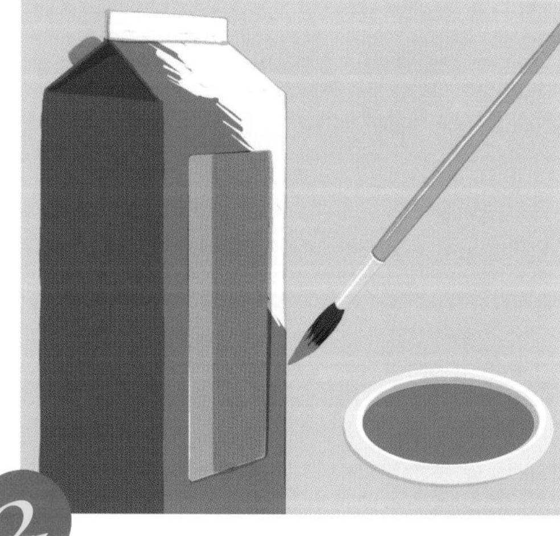

2 Paint the carton brown all over. Leave it to dry.

3 Add long streaks of dark brown and white and small brown knots to look like bark.

Top Tip Add a coat of varnish to help your feeder withstand the weather.

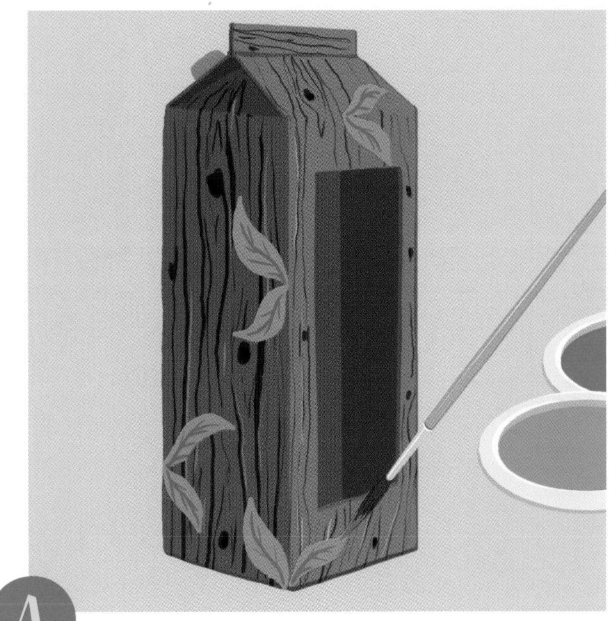

4

Paint leaves over the carton in light green, with darker green veins.

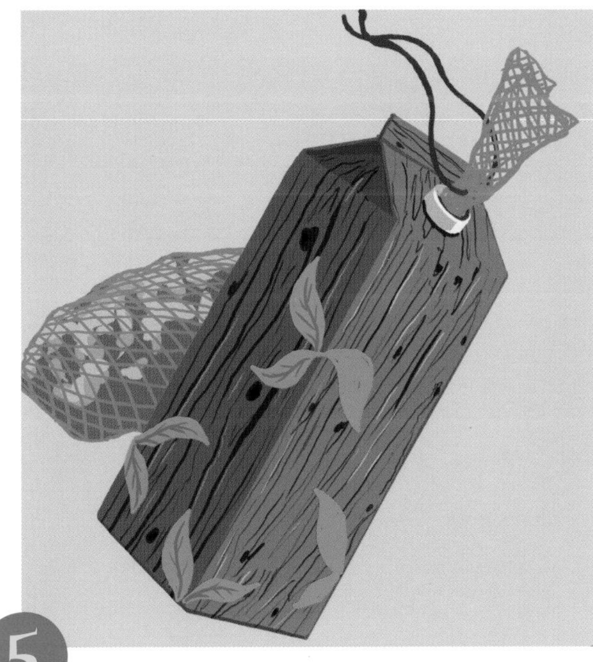

5

Push a bag of seeds through the window and pull the top through the spout. Thread wire through the top of the bag and twist the ends together. Hang the feeder up in the garden.

Yogurt pot herb garden

These dotty pots, planted with scrumptious herbs, will look great in the kichen window. Don't forget to water them!

You Will Need

- 3 yogurt pots
- Sandpaper
- Acrylic paints: red, green, yellow, white
- 3 jar lids
- Potted herbs: basil, oregano, chives
- Potting compost
- Bradawl or screwdriver

1

Wash and dry the pots and rub all over the outsides with sandpaper. This will help paint to stay on the pots.

2

Get an adult to help with this part. Make holes in the bottom of each pot with a bradawl or screwdriver.

3

Paint two coats on the outside of the pots: one each of yellow, green and red. When the paint has dried, dab white dots on each pot.

4

Paint some jar lids to make matching saucers.

5

Carefully remove the herbs from their pots and replant them. Add extra potting compost to fill the pots. Press it down and water the herbs well.

Top Tip

Herbs taste great: try adding basil to tomato pasta sauce – it's yummy! Oregano is perfect for pizzas, and snipped chives are delicious sprinkled on top of creamy potato salad.

RECYCLE IT!

Blazing pumps

Use fabric paint straight from the tube to make flaming streaks and a scary skull design on your pumps. They'll help you run like the blazes!

You Will Need

- Pair of black pumps
- Relief fabric paints: white, red, orange and yellow

1 Use the white paint to draw a skull outline on the front of each shoe. Then fill in the skulls, leaving circles for the eye sockets and a double row of teeth.

2 With the red paint, draw flames on either side of the skulls. Fill in the bottom of the flames in red and leave to dry.

3 Use the orange paint to fill in the middle part of each flame and leave to dry.

4

Finish by filling in the last sections using the yellow paint. Leave the pumps to dry.

Try This!

Party pumps

If you prefer a pretty princess look, stick on gems and use fabric relief pens to cover ballet pumps in a dotty flower pattern.

Top Tip

Sometimes the paint shrinks a little as it dries. Simply wait until the paint has dried completely then touch in some fresh paint.

RECYCLE IT!

Denim phone holder

Don't throw your old jeans away – you can turn them into all kinds of useful stuff, such as this cool mobile-phone holder.

You Will Need

- Old piece of denim
- Zig-zag scissors
- Red wool: 3 x 80cm lengths
- Needle and red thread
- Button
- Fabric glue
- Scrap of red felt
- Scissors
- Craft knife

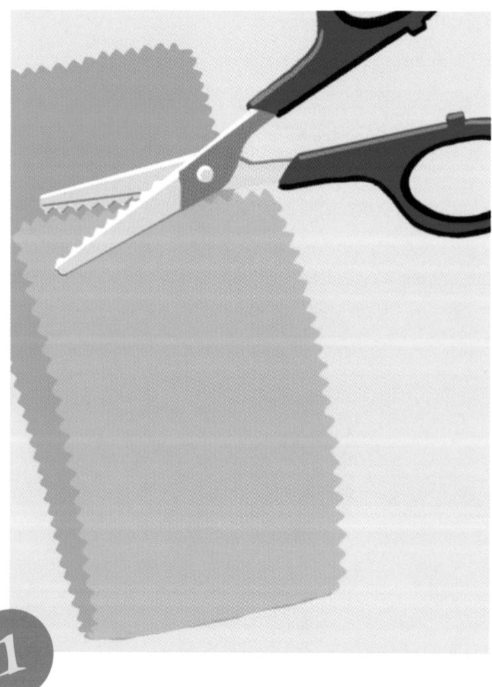

1 Cut the denim to 30 x 10cm using zig-zag scissors. Fold the fabric, leaving a flap at the top.

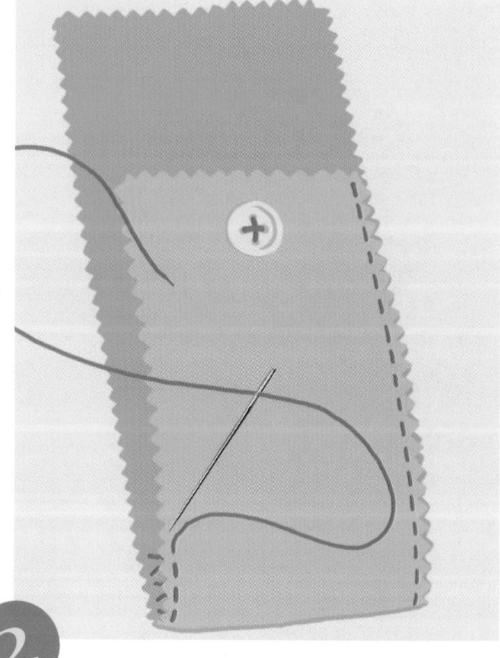

2 Use a needle and red thread to sew up each side of the holder. Sew a small button onto the front.

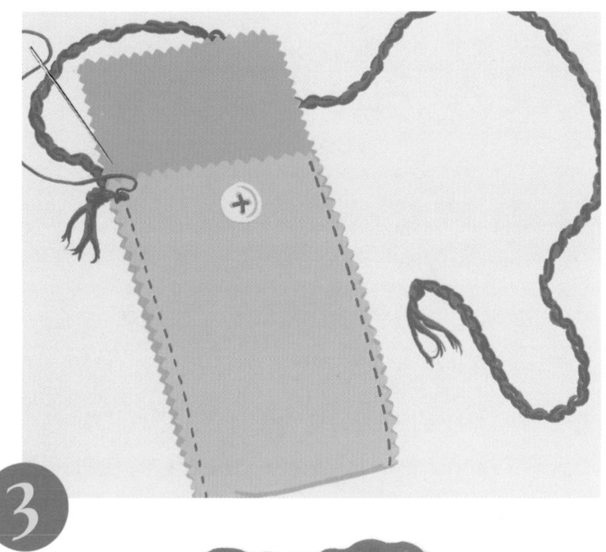

3

Make a plaited string. Put the three lengths of red wool together and tie a knot at one end. Plait the strands together and knot the other end. Stitch the plait to either side of the holder.

4

Cut out butterfly shapes from the red felt. Fold over the top flap and glue a butterfly over where you can feel the button underneath. Glue the other butterfly at the bottom of the bag.

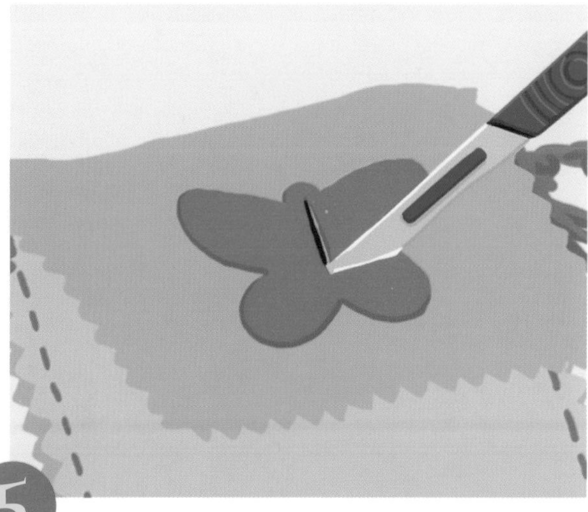

5

Ask an adult to cut a slit in the top butterfly to make a buttonhole.

RECYCLE IT!

Matchbox chest of drawers

You can store all sorts of things in this chest, from paper clips to buttons. And if you're a stamp collector, it's perfect for keeping your collection tidy.

You Will Need

- 6 empty matchboxes
- PVA glue and brush
- Selection of old/used stamps
- Scissors
- 6 paper fasteners

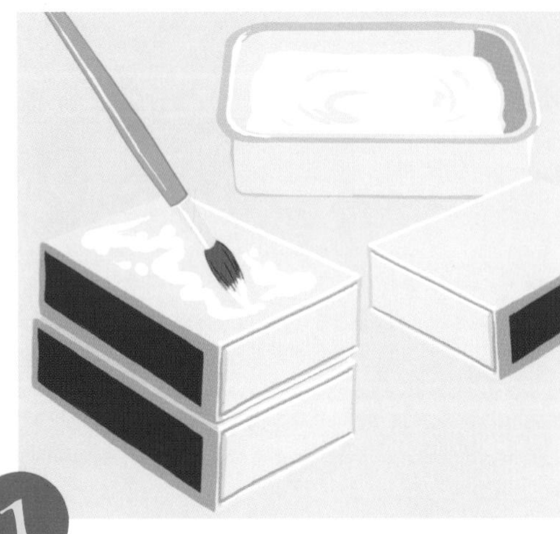

1 Glue three of the matchboxes together on top of one another. Do the same with the other three matchboxes.

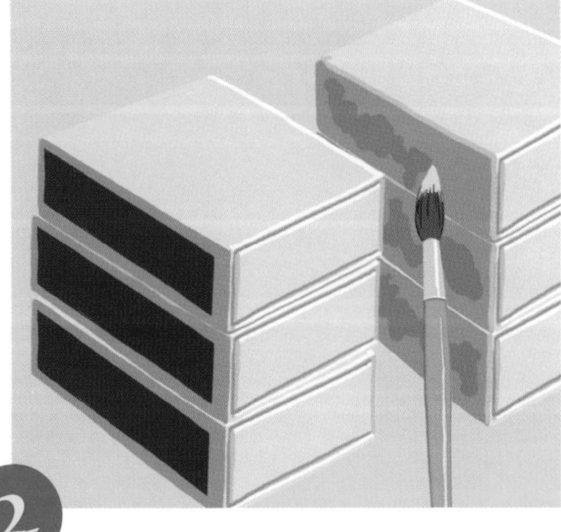

2 Glue the two sets of matchboxes together side by side. Leave to dry.

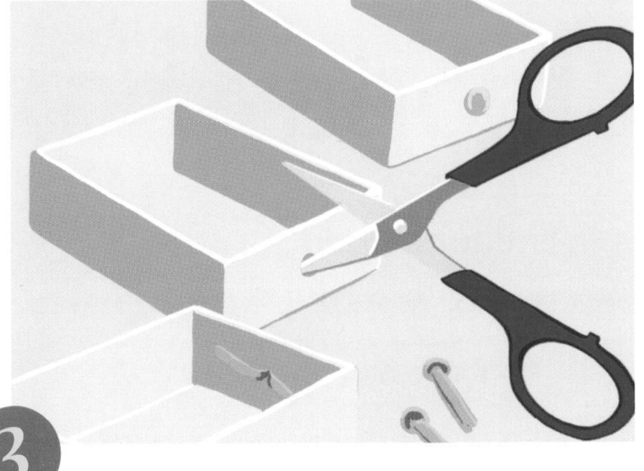

3

Remove the drawers. Use the end of a small pair of scissors to make a hole in the middle of each drawer. Push a paper fastener into each hole and bend the ends to fix them in place.

4

Paste the backs of the stamps with glue and stick them on the matchboxes. Overlap the stamps and stick them on at different angles.

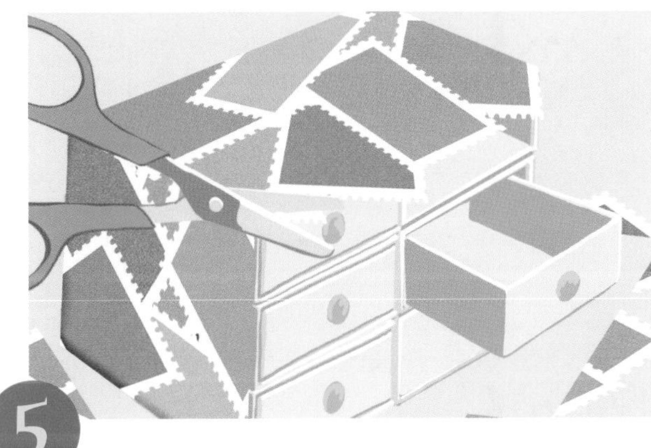

5

Trim the stamps where they overlap the edges of the box. Put the drawers back inside the boxes.

Try This!

Doll's house drawers

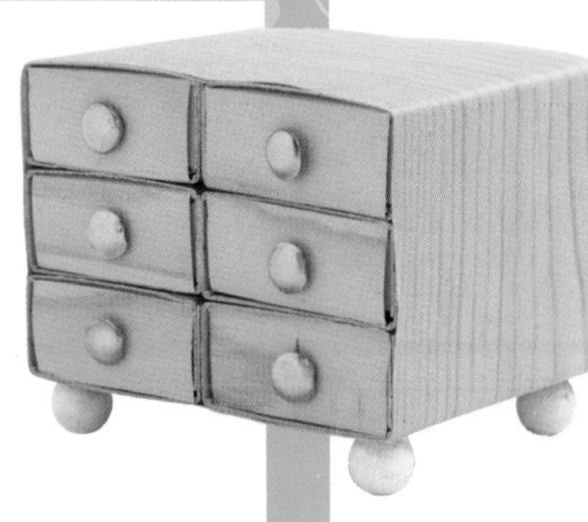

To make a doll's house chest of drawers, cut a piece of coloured or wood-grained paper to fit around the box and the drawer fronts and stick on with the glue. Glue four beads to the base for legs.

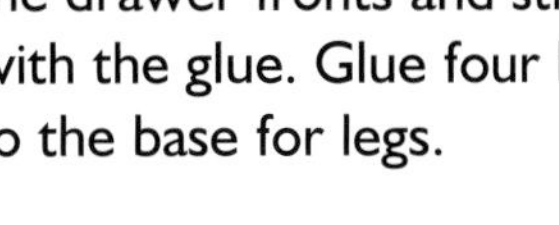

Stripey money box

Save your spare coins in a cool striped money bank made from a recycled round cocoa box. You'll be rich before you know it!

You Will Need

- Empty cardboard container with lid (eg. cocoa box)
- Ruler and pencil
- A4 sheets of coloured paper
- PVA glue and brush
- Craft knife or scalpel

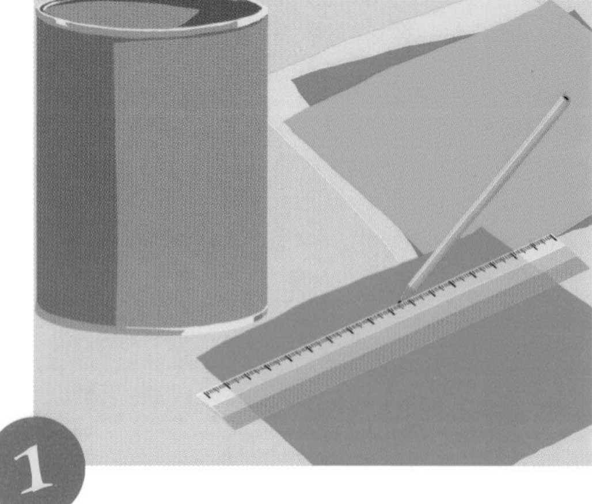

1

Measure the height of the tin and cut the paper to the same height. Draw lines down one of the sheets, changing the distance between the lines to make narrower and wider stripes.

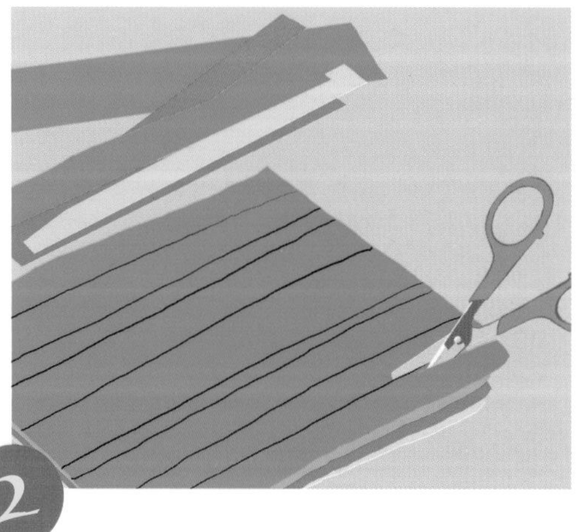

2

Put the ruled sheet on top of the others and cut along the lines to make long strips.

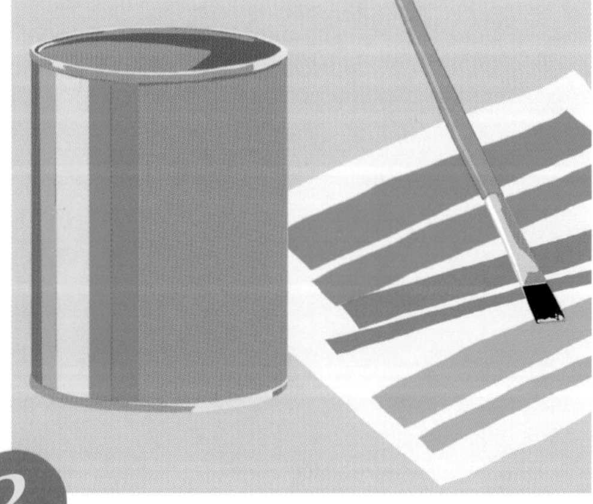

3

Paste the strips with glue and stick them to the box, making sure they overlap and smoothing them down carefully.

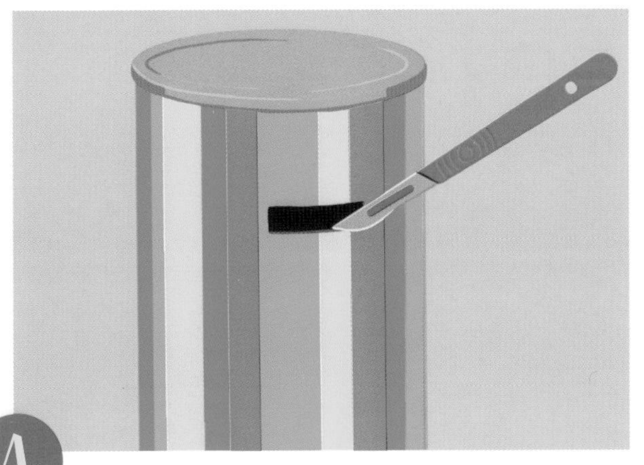

4

When the glue has dried, ask an adult to cut a money slot measuring about 45 x 7mm.

Try This!

Extra safe

If you're always raiding your money bank, make this no-lid version from a cereal bar box. Use parcel tape to seal it, then decorate with the paper strips. You'll have to break the whole box to get your hands on the cash!

Tiger feet

It's easy to turn old tissue boxes into stripey tiger's feet complete with scary claws – they're grrrr-eat!

You Will Need

- 2 empty tissue boxes
- Acrylic paints: yellow, orange, black, white
- Paintbrush and old sponge
- Black funky foam and 10 sticky tabs
- Scissors
- Glue

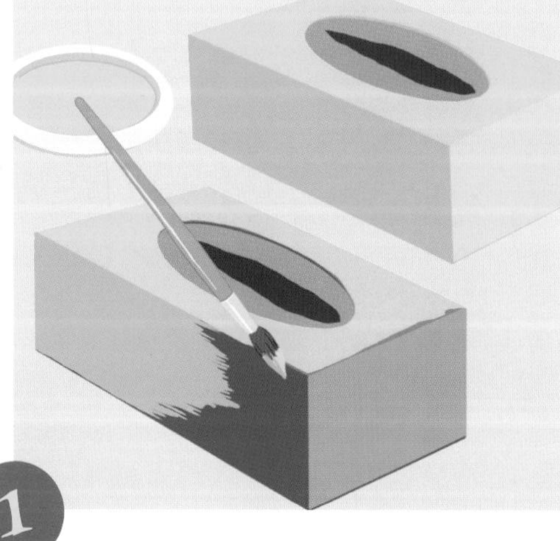

1 Using the yellow acrylic paint, paint the top and sides of the tissue boxes. Leave to dry. Apply another coat if the box colour still shows through.

2 Dip a dry sponge in orange paint and dab it sparingly all over the boxes.

3

Paint black stripes about 15mm wide all over the boxes, tapering them at the ends. Don't worry if they aren't neat, as this will make the stripes look more natural. Dab a few short white stripes on the edges of the black stripes.

4

Cut four pointed claws for each foot from the black foam. Make each one slightly smaller than the last. Stick them onto the box using sticky tabs. Put the biggest claw on opposite sides of each box so you have a right and left foot.

Try This!

Zebra tissue holder

Make a zebra-striped tissue box by painting a full box of tissues white. After the white paint is dry, add black tapering stripes all over the box.

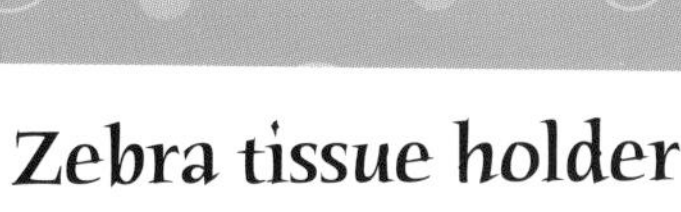

Racing yachts

These great little yachts are made from corks, and no matter what you do, they'll never sink. Try it and see!

You Will Need

For each yacht:

- 3 corks
- All-purpose glue
- 2 lolly sticks
- Cocktail stick
- Scraps of coloured paper

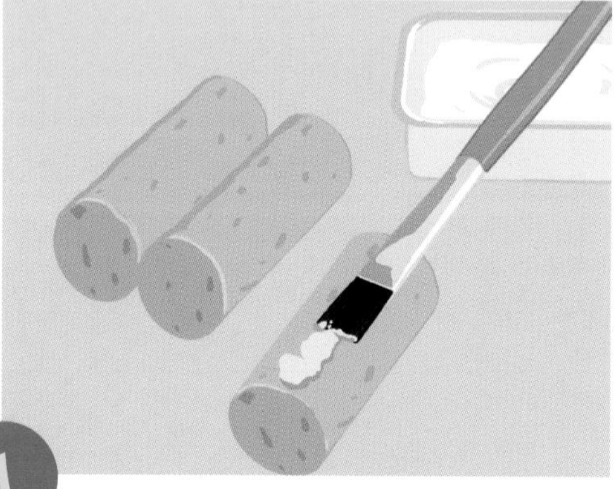

1

Glue the three corks together, side by side, using the strong glue. Leave to dry.

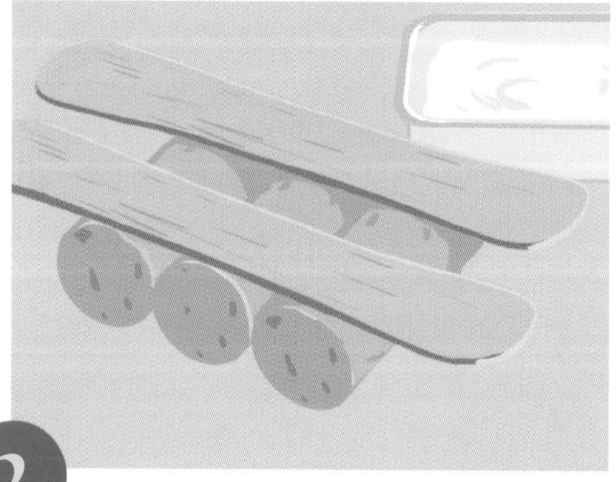

2

Glue the two lolly sticks to the top of the corks as shown. Leave to dry.

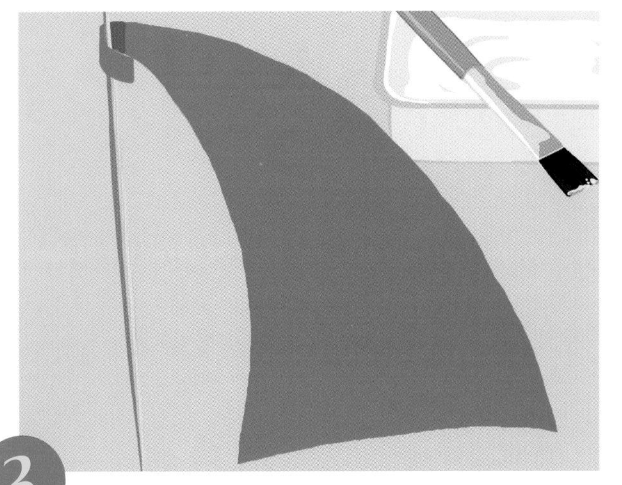

3 While the glue is drying, cut a triangular sail from one of the scraps of coloured paper. Apply a little glue to the tip of the sail and wrap it round the top of the cocktail stick. Leave to dry.

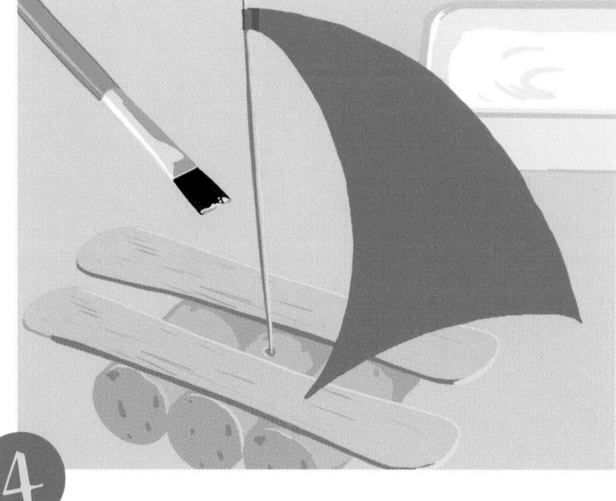

4 Make a hole in the centre of the middle cork between the lolly sticks. Push the cocktail-stick mast firmly into the hole. Bend the sail round so it sits on the top of the boat.

5 Cut a tiny triangle in yellow paper and glue to the top of the cocktail stick mast to make a flag.

Try This!

One-cork yacht

If you don't have lots of corks, make a simpler version using just one. Push three map tacks in a row along the bottom of the cork to help your yacht stay upright.

RECYCLE IT!

Sporty storage box

This box will keep all your sports stuff together ready for your next game. Make your room really tidy by making a matching toy box decorated with toy shapes!

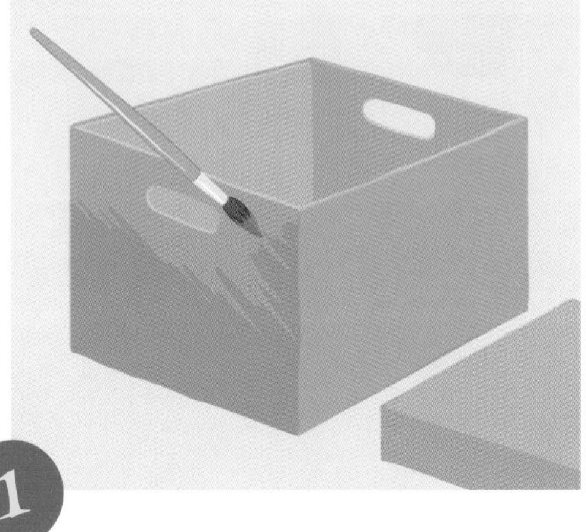

1

Paint the box and the lid all over in green. Leave to dry, then paint another coat.

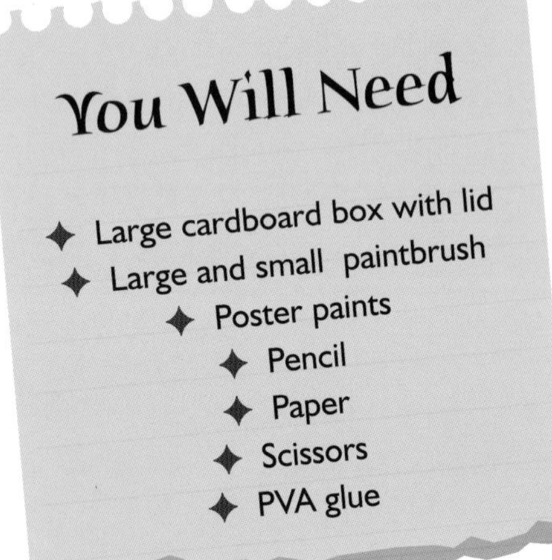

You Will Need

- Large cardboard box with lid
- Large and small paintbrush
- Poster paints
- Pencil
- Paper
- Scissors
- PVA glue

2

Draw the outlines of different sports balls and a tennis racquet onto a sheet of white paper. Cut them out.

3

Use paints and a smaller brush to put the details on to the shapes.

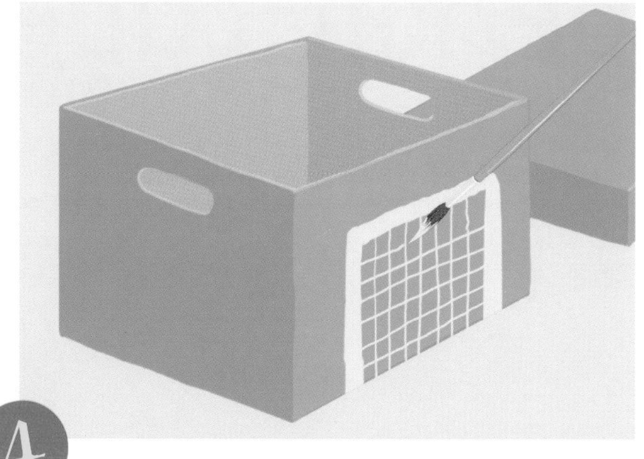

4

Paint a large white goal onto the front of the box.

5

Arrange all the sporting shapes round the box and glue them on. Leave it to dry, then get tidying!

RECYCLE IT!

Starry pencil tube

Now you have a perfect excuse to eat a whole tube of crisps – you can use the empty tube to make a cool pencil case!

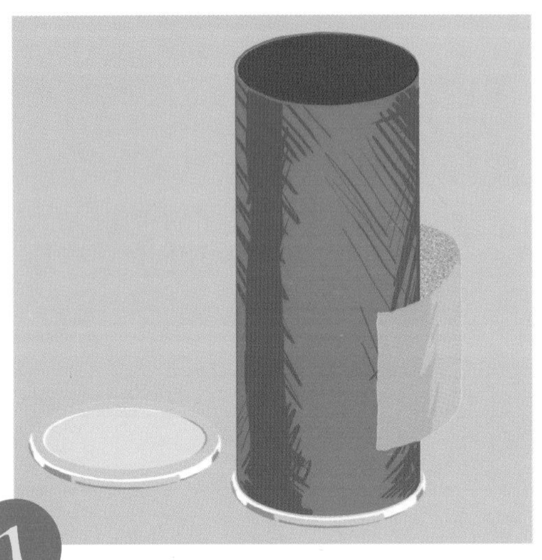

1

Rub the tube all over with sandpaper. This will help the paint stick better to the tube.

You Will Need

- ✦ Cardboard crisp tube with lid
- ✦ Fine sandpaper
- ✦ Black acrylic paint
- ✦ Paintbrush
- ✦ PVA glue
- ✦ Glitter: gold, silver
- ✦ Scrap paper
- ✦ Sequins and star stickers

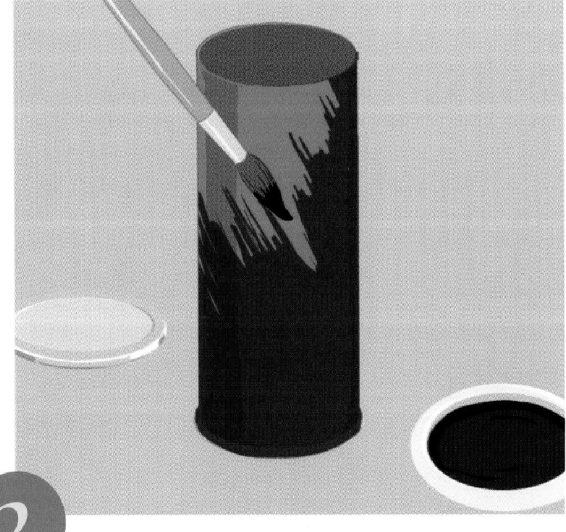

2

Cover the tube in black acrylic paint. Leave to dry, then give it another coat.

3

Make three swirls of glue, like the tail of a comet. Sprinkle gold glitter over the glue and shake off the excess onto scrap paper. Repeat with silver glitter on other parts of the tube.

Ribbon pattern

Make an abstract stripey pattern on your pencil case. Paint the tube green, then glue on long strips of coloured paper in a random pattern.

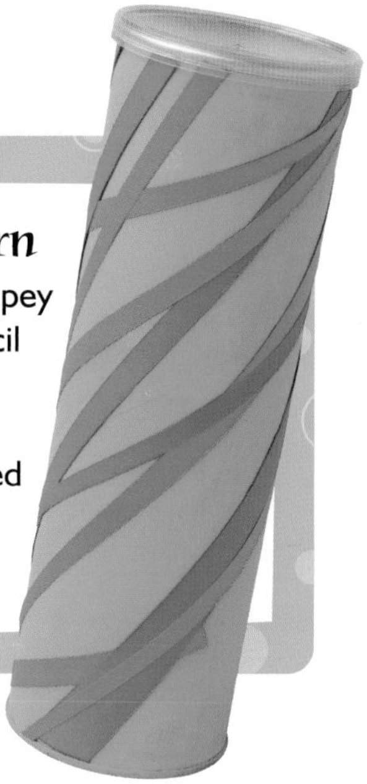

Top Tip

Perfect for pasta

A crisp tube also is an ideal shape for storing long spaghetti. It would make a great gift for the chef in your family.

4

Stick small groups of stars on to make the heads of the comets. Stick other stars randomly on the tube. Glue a row of sequins round the top and bottom of the pencil case.

Lolly-stick pencil pot

You Will Need

- Empty tube (eg. a biscuit tube)
- About 30 identical lolly sticks
- Small set square
- PVA glue and brush

To make this pencil holder, you have to collect lots of lolly sticks. Better get munching!

1

Wash the lolly sticks and tin in warm soapy water. Dry thoroughly. Apply glue to one side of one of the lolly sticks. Line up the set square against the can and stick the glued lolly stick in place, butting it up to the set square.

2

Glue the sticks round the can, until you have only 3-4 cms of blank can showing.

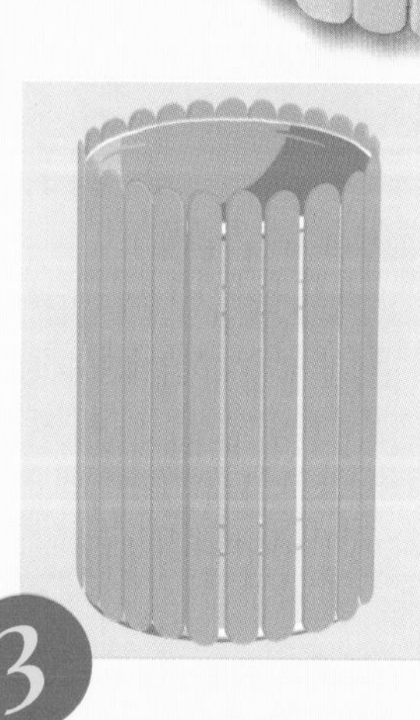

3

◂ Paste glue onto three or four sticks and arrange them in the gap, spacing them out evenly to fill the space.

FOOD FUN

FOOD FUN

Peppermint creams

You'll need an adult's help to make these scrummy sweets, but you won't need any help to eat them!

You Will Need

For 20 sweets:

- ✦ 450g icing sugar
- ✦ 1 egg white
- ✦ Juice of half a lemon
- ✦ A few drops of peppermint essence and green food colour
- ✦ Bar of cooking chocolate
- ✦ Sieve, bowl, cookie cutter, wooden spoon

1 Sieve the icing sugar into a large mixing bowl.

2 Separate the egg yolk from the white – get an adult to help you with this. Add the egg white to the icing sugar.

3 Mix it all together with your hands until you have made a soft lump. Add the lemon juice, peppermint essence and green colour.

4

Tip the lump out onto a cold surface and flatten it to about 1cm thick. Cut out the shapes, put them on a tray and leave them in a cool, dry place to set.

5

Break up the bar of chocolate and put in it a bowl. Put the bowl over a saucepan of simmering water and stir the chocolate until it has melted.

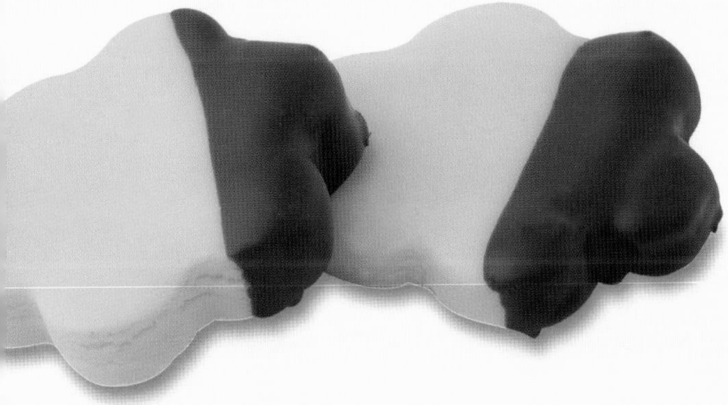

6

Take the bowl off the heat and quickly dip half of each sweet into the chocolate. Leave the sweets until the chocolate hardens.

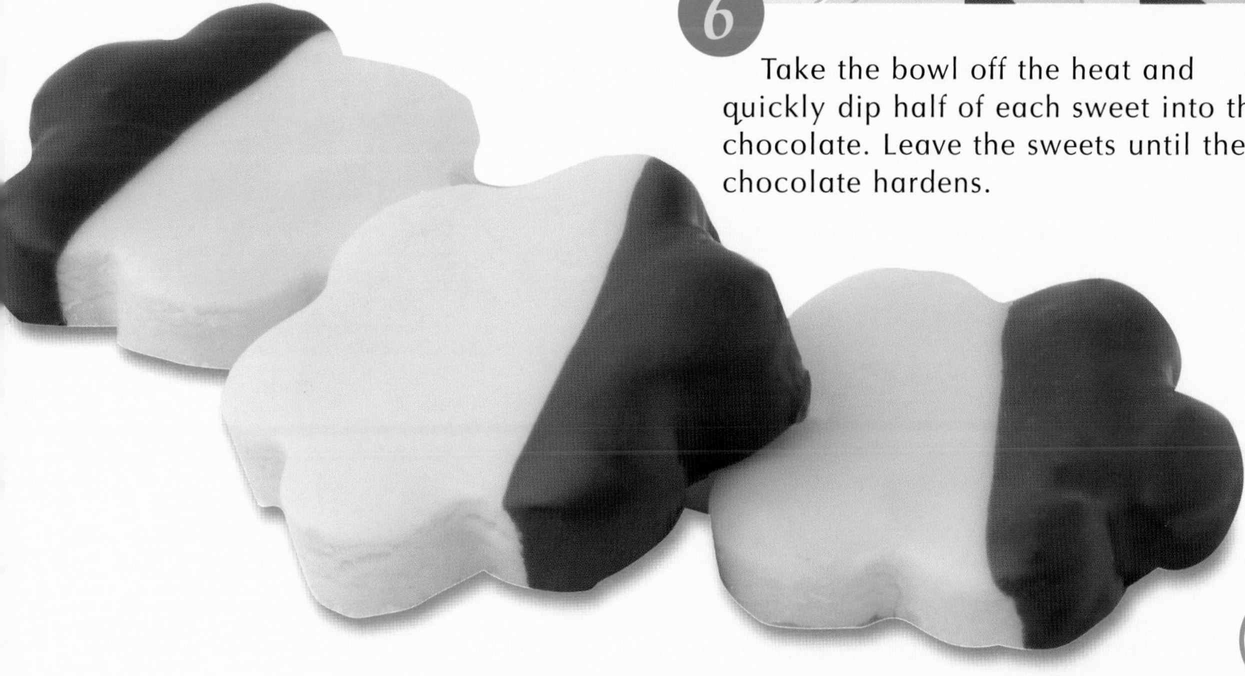

FOOD FUN

Fruit smoothies

Get an adult to help with the chopping, then whisk yourself a delicious, healthy fruit drink!

You Will Need

For the strawberry smoothie:

- 4 strawberries
- 100g fresh mango
- 1 small banana
- Juice of 1 orange
- 3 tbsp yogurt
- 1 tbsp honey
- Hand blender with pot
- Glass and straws

1

Chop three strawberries, the mango and the banana. Put them in the bowl with all the other ingredients.

2

Blend everything until you have a smooth, runny mixture.

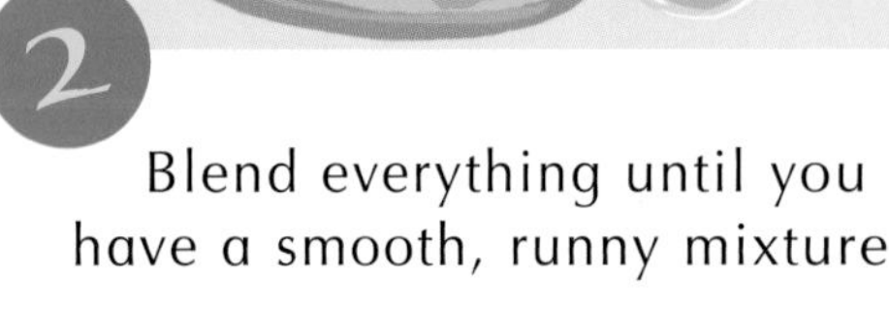

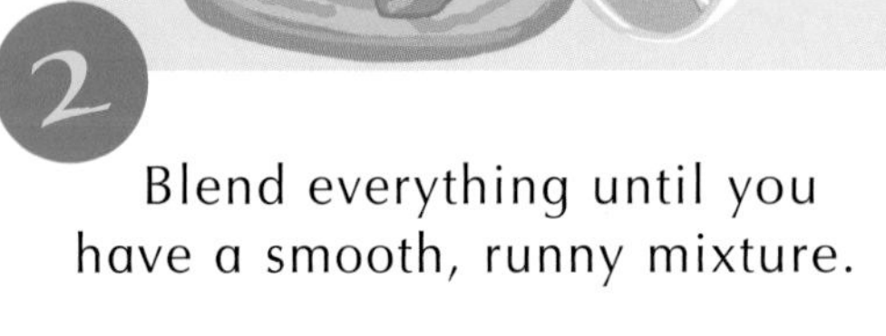

3

Pour the smoothie mixture into a glass. Cut the remaining strawberry in half and use it to decorate the glass. Add colourful straws.

Try This!

Frozen treats

Why not make delicious fruit smoothie ice lollies? Just pour the smoothie mixture into an ice-lolly tray, add a stick, and pop it in the freezer!

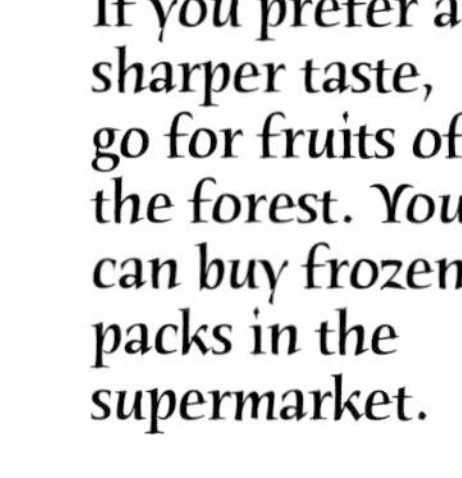
If you prefer a sharper taste, go for fruits of the forest. You can buy frozen packs in the supermarket.

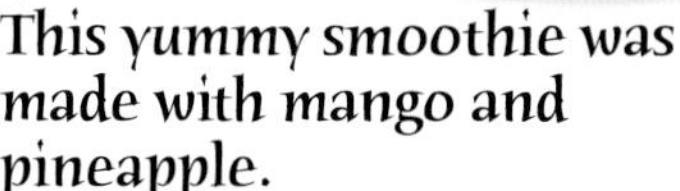
This yummy smoothie was made with mango and pineapple.

Pasta jewellery

Pasta comes in so many shapes and sizes that you can make a different necklace for every outfit!

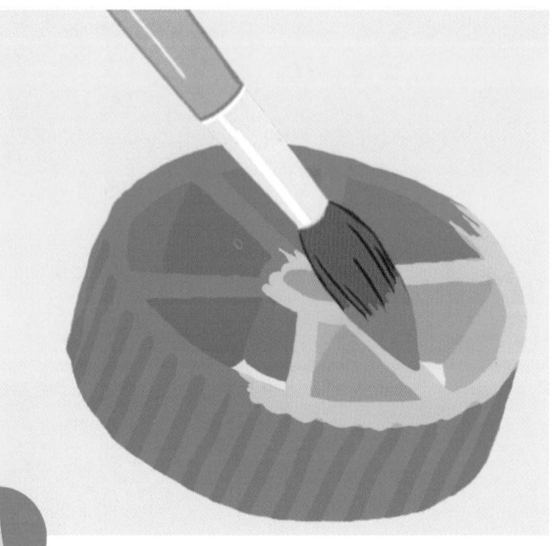

1

Paint the pasta wheels in green, blue and purple acrylic paint.

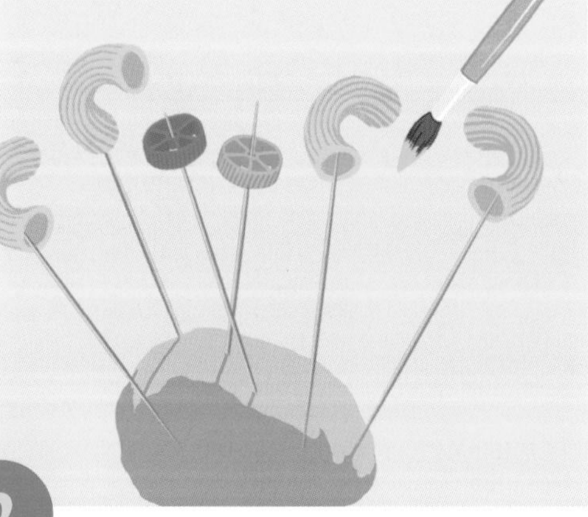

2

Paint the macaroni gold, and put all the shapes on the ends of cocktail sticks stuck in plasticine to dry.

You Will Need

- ✦ Dried pasta shapes: 6 wheels, 24 curly macaroni
- ✦ Acrylic paints: green, blue, purple, gold
- ✦ Lump of plasticine
- ✦ Cocktail sticks
- ✦ Coloured stiff elastic or cord

Tie a button to the thread while you thread the shapes to stop them falling off!

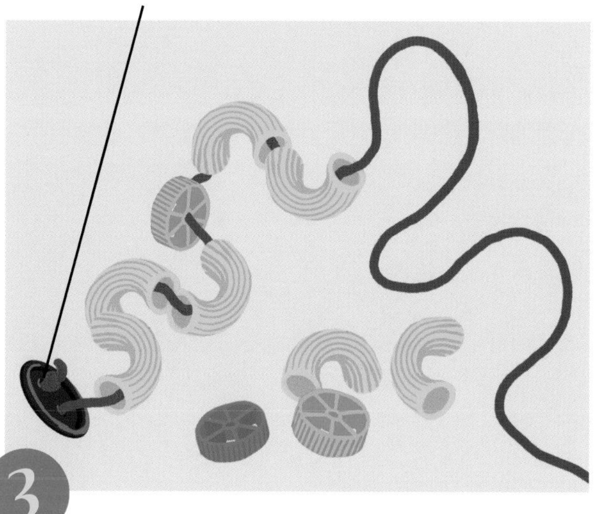

3

Thread three macaronis then a wheel onto the coloured thread. Repeat this until all the jewels are threaded.

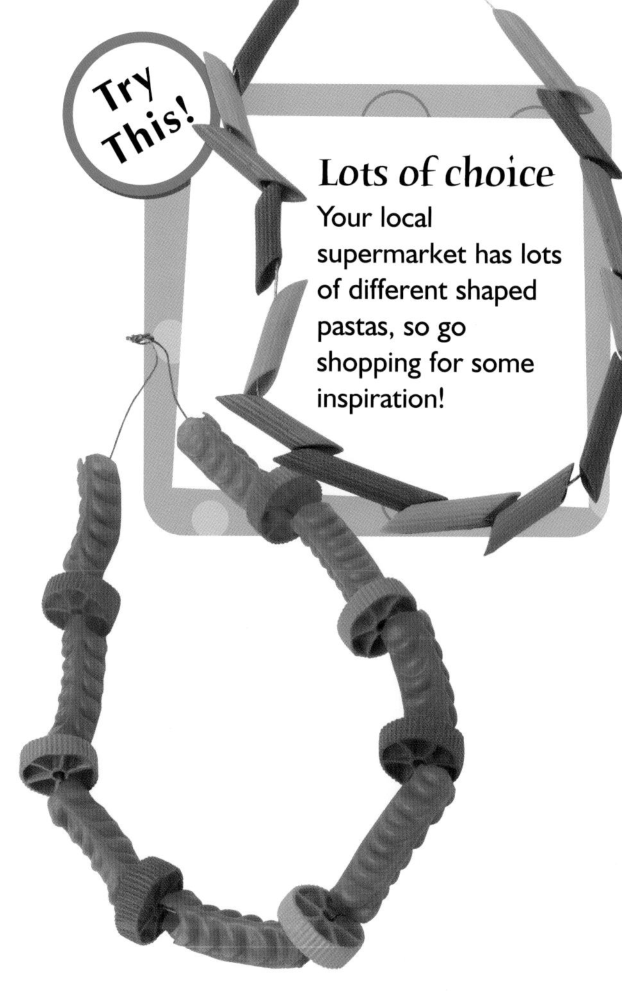

Try This!

Lots of choice

Your local supermarket has lots of different shaped pastas, so go shopping for some inspiration!

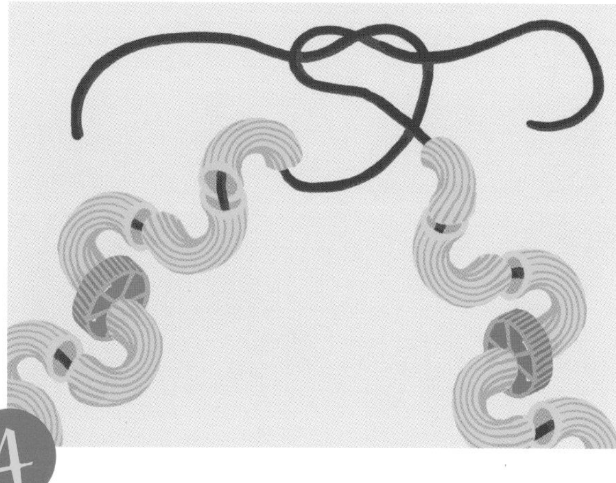

4

Knot the two ends of the thread together, making sure you have made your necklace big enough to go over your head.

Gingerbread Men

If you want to make this project even quicker to do, get an icing pen from the supermarket – they're cheap and easy to use.

1

Heat the butter and sugar gently in a pan until the sugar dissolves and the butter melts.

You Will Need

- 30g butter
- 60g brown sugar
- 4 tbsp black treacle
- 150g plain flour
- Pinch of salt
- ½ tsp baking powder, ginger, cinnamon
- Gingerbread man cutter
- Rolling pin, baking sheet, sieve, bowl, saucepan
- Icing: 50g icing sugar, water, food colour and small greaseproof paper bag, or an icing pen

2

Sift all the other ingredients into a large bowl. Add the melted mixture and mix it all together until you have a soft ball of dough. Put it in the fridge for an hour.

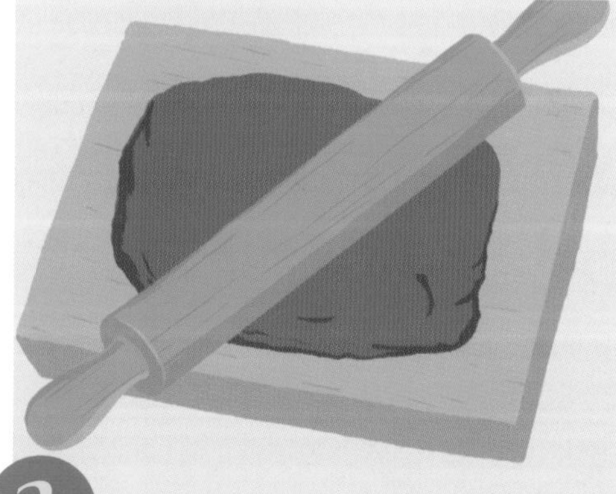

3

Roll the dough out to about 2cm thick.

4

Use the cutter to make shapes in the dough. Put them on a greased baking sheet and bake them at 170°C for 5 minutes.

5

While the biscuits cool, make the icing. Sift icing sugar into a bowl, add a few drops of blue food colour and a little water and mix until you have a thick paste.

6

When the cookies are cold, snip the corner off a paper bag and spoon the icing in. Decorate your gingerbread man by squeezing the bag gently so that the icing comes out of the snipped corner.

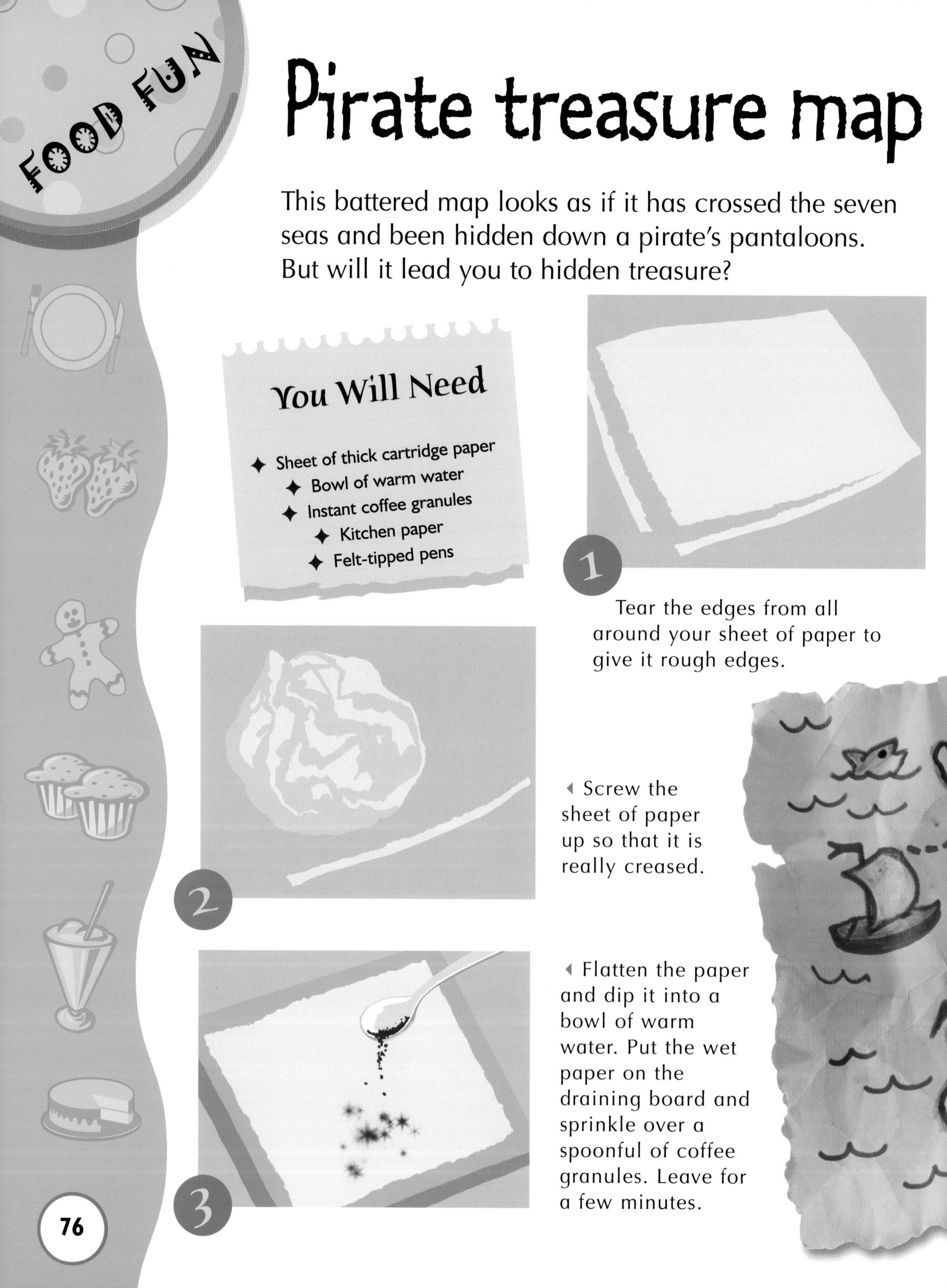

Pirate treasure map

This battered map looks as if it has crossed the seven seas and been hidden down a pirate's pantaloons. But will it lead you to hidden treasure?

You Will Need

- Sheet of thick cartridge paper
- Bowl of warm water
- Instant coffee granules
- Kitchen paper
- Felt-tipped pens

1. Tear the edges from all around your sheet of paper to give it rough edges.

2. Screw the sheet of paper up so that it is really creased.

3. Flatten the paper and dip it into a bowl of warm water. Put the wet paper on the draining board and sprinkle over a spoonful of coffee granules. Leave for a few minutes.

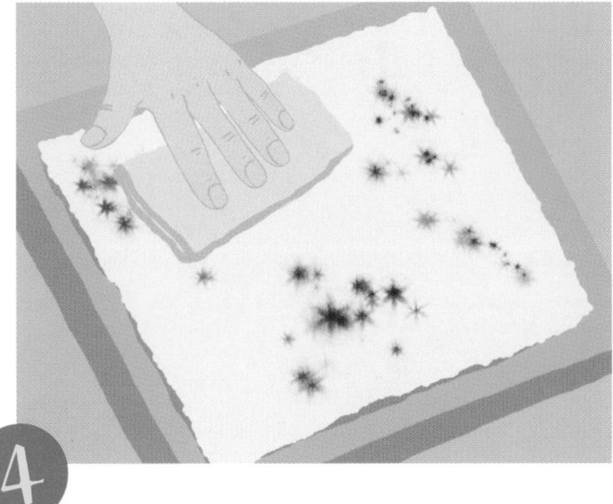

4

Dab the stains with kitchen paper then dip the paper in a bowl of warm water. Repeat the staining and rinsing on the other side of the paper. Leave it to dry out.

5

Draw a treasure map like the one shown. Add dangerous areas with a skull and crossbones and mark the hidden treasure with a big X.

Try This!

Skull seal

To keep your map secret, roll it up and tie it with ribbon. Add a scary skull and crossbones seal made from modelling clay.

Fishy burgers

Everyone will love these delicious, healthy burgers. If you like veggy food, mash up a can of kidney beans and use them instead of the salmon.

You Will Need

To make 4 burgers:

- I small onion, chopped
- Pinch of mixed herbs
- A large handful of breadcrumbs
- 212g tin of red salmon
- I egg
- Salt and pepper
- A little flour
- Frying pan and a little oil
- Lettuce, tomatoes, onion rings, mayonnaise
- Burger bun

1

Get an adult to help with the cooking. Heat the oil, add the onion, herbs and breadcrumbs and cook gently for 5 minutes.

2

◂ Tip the mixture into a bowl and add the salmon, egg and a little salt and pepper. Mix everything together with your hands.

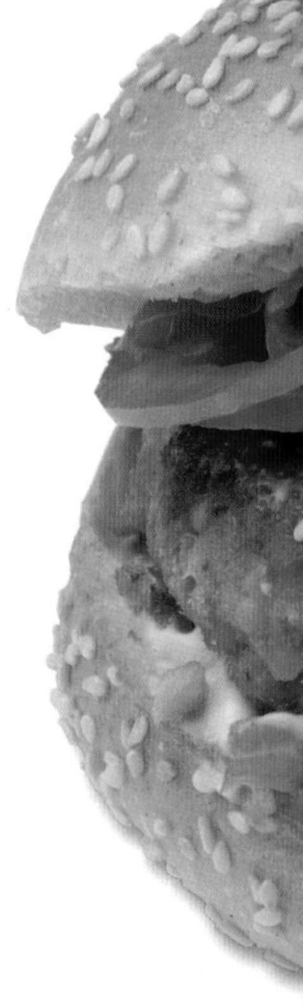

3

Sprinkle some flour onto a work surface and shape the mixture into burger shapes, using clean hands.

Top Tip

Make your burgers with tuna instead of salmon if you prefer.

4

Wash and dry the frying pan, add a little more oil and put the pan on a medium heat. Fry the burger for five minutes on each side.

5

Put each burger onto a bun and garnish with your favourite salad ingredients.

FOOD FUN

Choc chip cookies

These star-shaped cookies are magic – they disappear in seconds! Mix in a handful of raisins or nuts instead of the chocolate for a tasty change.

You Will Need

- 300g plain flour
- Pinch of salt
- I ttsp baking powder
- 100g butter
- 100g light brown sugar
- 2 beaten eggs
- 60g golden syrup
- 75g chocolate
- Rolling pin
- Star cookie cutter

1 Sieve the flour, salt and baking powder into a large bowl.

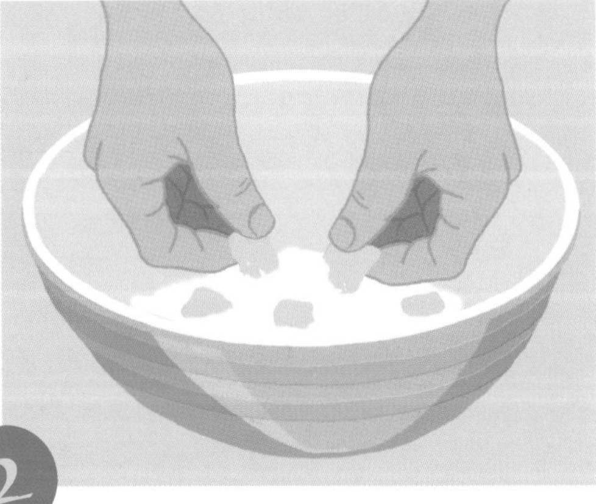

2 Rub in the butter with your hands, then add the sugar. Stir a beaten egg and the syrup together and add to the bowl.

3 Beat the mixture well with a wooden spoon. Add the other beaten egg. Break the chocolate into small pieces and add to the mixture.

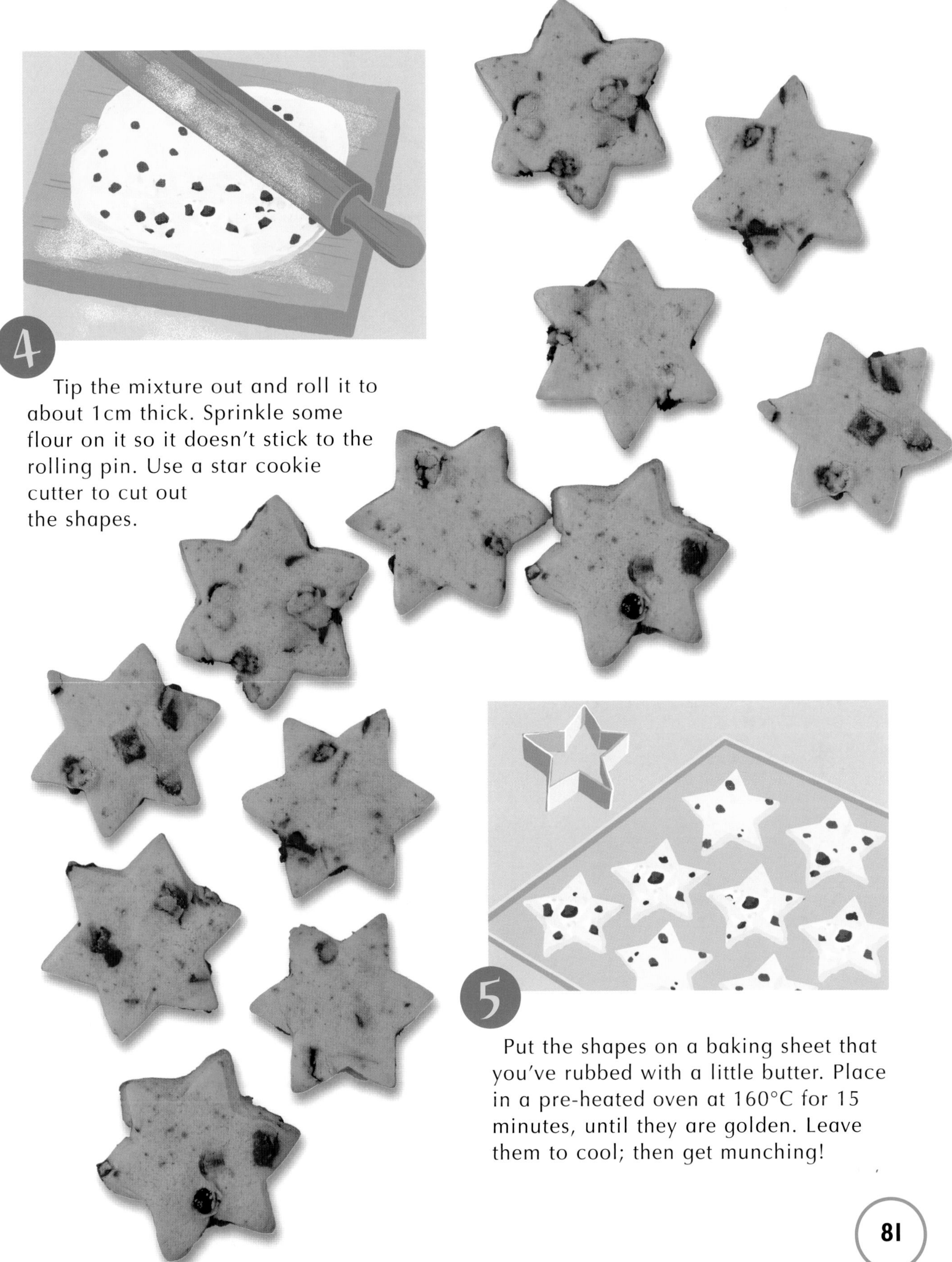

4

Tip the mixture out and roll it to about 1cm thick. Sprinkle some flour on it so it doesn't stick to the rolling pin. Use a star cookie cutter to cut out the shapes.

5

Put the shapes on a baking sheet that you've rubbed with a little butter. Place in a pre-heated oven at 160°C for 15 minutes, until they are golden. Leave them to cool; then get munching!

Printed T-shirt

Do you think vegetables are yucky? Think again! They are perfect for making prints. Try this froggy T-shirt and see for yourself.

1

Get an adult to help with this part. Cut the two potatoes in half and trim the top of the celery. Cut a 3cm piece of carrot; then cut it in half lengthways.

You Will Need

- ✦ T-shirt
- ✦ Piece of scrap card
- ✦ Vegetables: 1 large and 1 small potato, 1 stick of celery, 1 carrot
- ✦ Chopping board and knife
- ✦ Green fabric paint
- ✦ Shallow dish
- ✦ Tube of fabric relief paint metallic blue

2

Put a scrap of card inside the shirt to stop the paint seeping through. Pour some of the green paint into the dish. Dip a larger potato half into the paint, dab off any excess on the side of the plate and make a print in the centre of the T-shirt. This will be the body of the frog.

3

Use one of the small potato halves to print the two back legs.Dip the top end of the celery stalk into the paint and use to print a bulging eye. Repeat for the other eye.

4 Use the carrot to print the lower back legs and the front legs, then cut the carrot piece in half to print the front and back feet. Leave to dry.

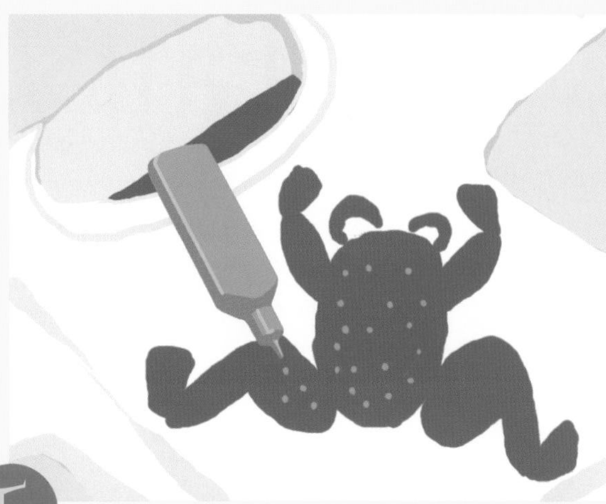

5 Dab tiny spots all over the frog, using the tube of fabric paint. Leave the T-shirt to dry.

Try This!

Green gecko

Once you've got the hang of veggie printing, try different designs. This cute gecko was also made with potato, carrot and celery, with yellow relief paint dotted over his body.

Fairy cakes

Get an adult to help you cook these scrummy cakes – they're fun to make and even more fun to eat!

You Will Need

For 12 cakes:

- 75g caster sugar
- 1 beaten egg
- Vanilla essence
- 75g self-raising flour
- Silver foil cases
- Wooden spoon, dessert spoon, baking sheet and cooling rack

For the icing:

- 60g icing sugar
- Few drops red food colouring
- Metallic cake decorations
- Butter knife

1

Mix the butter and sugar in a large bowl. Mix in the egg a little at a time. Add a few drops of vanilla essence.

2

Sieve the flour into the bowl and use a wooden spoon to mix it in gently.

3

Spoon a blob of mixture into each case. Put them on a baking sheet and cook in a pre-heated oven at 200°C for 10 minutes. Leave them to cool.

4

To make the icing, sieve the icing sugar into the bowl, add a few drops of food colour and just enough water to make a paste.

5

Spread the icing onto the cakes. Sprinkle metallic balls on top and leave the cakes to set. Yum!

Cress caterpillar

If you get fed up waiting for plants to grow, cress is the answer – it only takes a few days! It tastes great in salads and sandwiches, too.

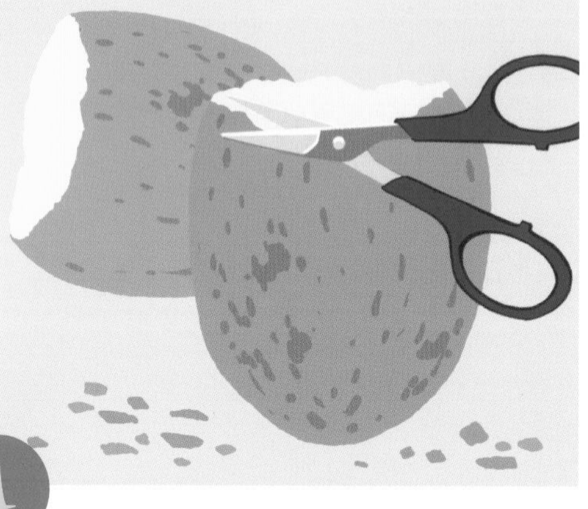

1

Take five clean, empty egg shells with their tops lopped off. Trim the tops with nail scissors.

You Will Need

- ✦ 5 egg shells
- ✦ Nail scissors
- ✦ Paints: green, red, black
- ✦ Googly eyes
- ✦ Paintbrush
- ✦ PVA glue
- ✦ Packet of cress seeds
- ✦ Cotton wool
- ✦ Red pipe cleaner

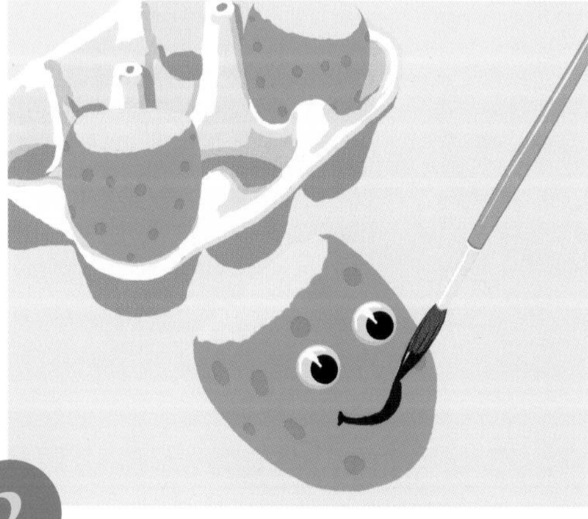

2

Paint the eggs green with red spots. Glue googly eyes to one of them and paint a black mouth. Put them in an egg box to dry.

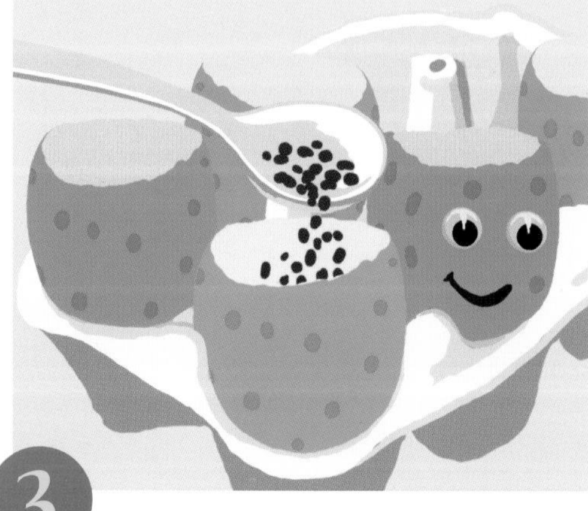

3

When they are dry, put a wad of cotton wool in the bottom of each egg, add 1tsp of cress seeds, then pour a spoonful of water over the cotton wool.

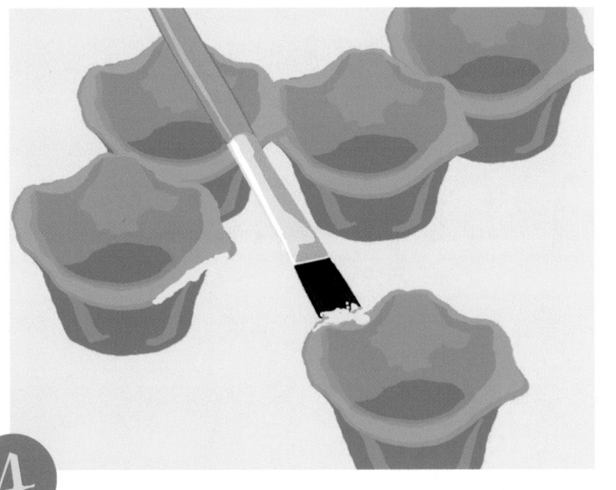

4

Cut up a cardboard egg box to make five little dishes. Paint them green and glue them together in a wiggly line.

5

Put an egg in each dish, with the face at the front. To make antennae, twist a pipe cleaner into spirals at both ends, fold it in half and push it into the face shell.

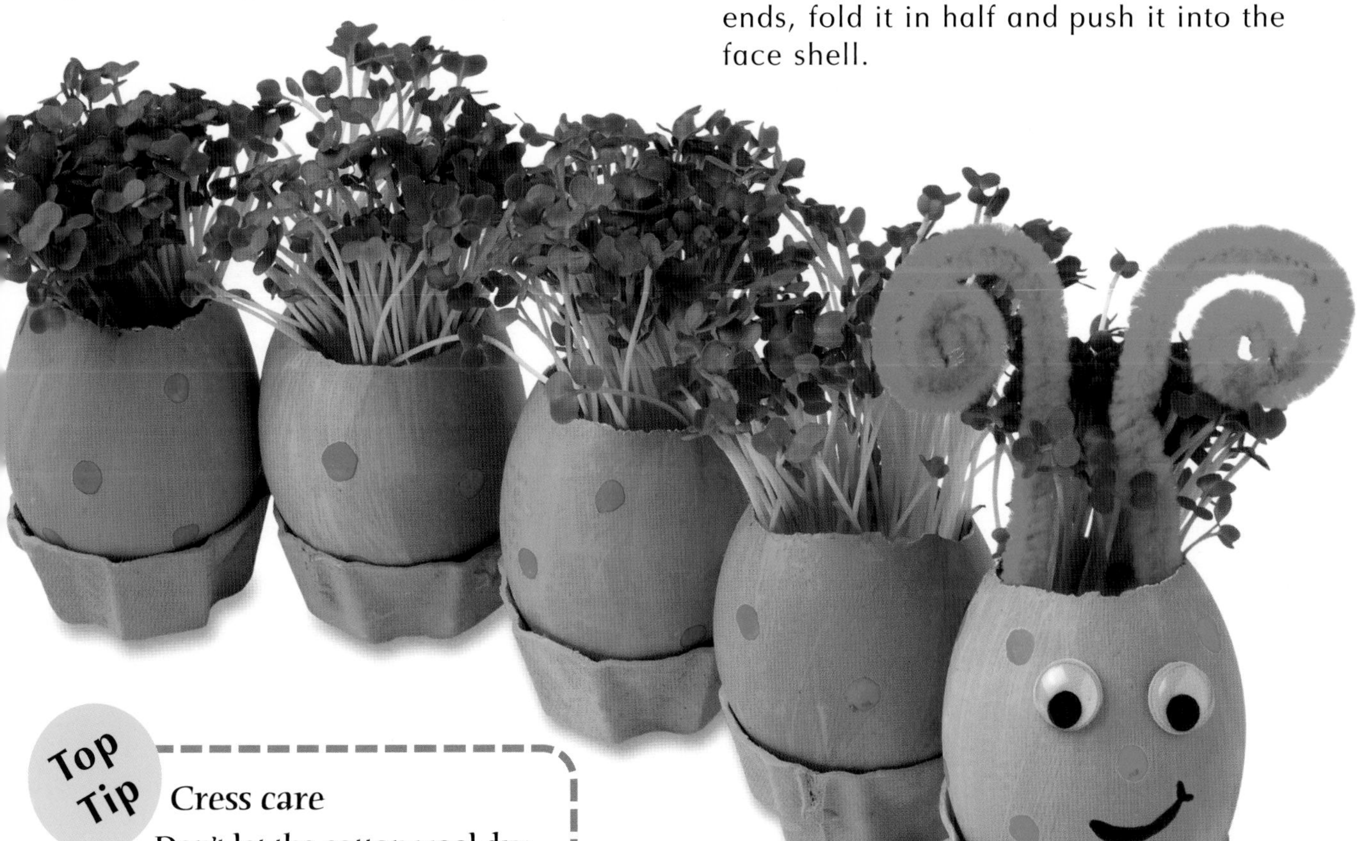

Top Tip

Cress care

Don't let the cotton wool dry out - add a little water every other day. The cress takes about a week to grow, then just snip it, wash it and enjoy!

FOOD FUN

Chocolate banana sundae

Try this easy recipe or have a sundae competition with your friends. Invent weird and wonderful combinations and vote for your favourite!

You Will Need

- Vanilla ice cream
- 1 banana
- Chocolate sauce
- Hundreds and thousands
- Sundae glass and spoon

1

Spoon the ice cream into the bottom of a sundae glass.

2

Add a layer of sliced banana and some chocolate sauce. Repeat the layers until you have only three slices of banana left.

This scrummy sundae is made with peach ice cream, peach slices and crushed meringue.

Fresh strawberries and raspberry ripple ice cream make a delicious fruity sundae

Top Tip Take the ice cream out of the freezer about 10 minutes before you start so it will be soft enough to spoon.

3

Decorate the top of the sundae with the banana slices, some more chocolate sauce and the hundreds and thousands.

Clove pomanders

One of these clove-scented natural air fresheners in your room will soon get rid of that pongy aroma of old trainers!

You Will Need

- Orange and lime
- ½ metre each of green and orange ribbon
- Cocktail stick
- Cloves

1 Put the orange in the middle of the green ribbon. Tie the ribbon in a knot, then tie a tight bow over the knot. Repeat for the lime, using the orange ribbon.

2 Use a cocktail stick to pierce the orange and push a clove into the hole. Make holes all over the orange, about 10mm apart. Repeat for the lime.

GREAT GIFTS

Fishy glitter globe

This is a great way to use glass paints. Design an ocean scene, fill a jar with glittery water and shake up a storm!

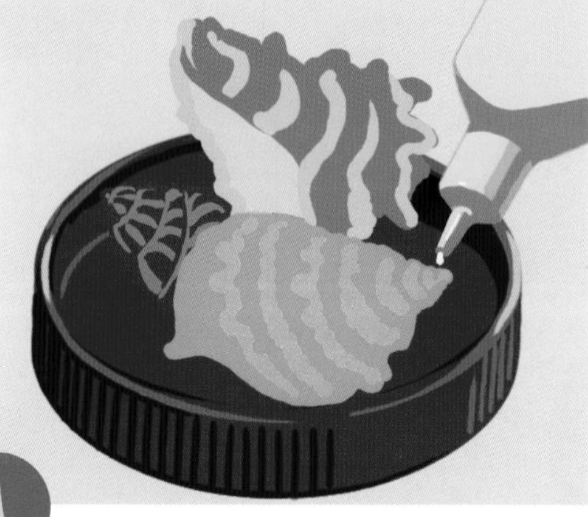

1 If you want, arrange shells on the inside of the jar lid. Glue them to the lid and leave to dry.

You Will Need

- Empty round jar and lid
- All-purpose waterproof glue
- Seashells (optional)
- Black relief outliner glass paint
- Glass paints: red, orange, green
- Paintbrush
- Glycerine
- Water
- Blue glitter

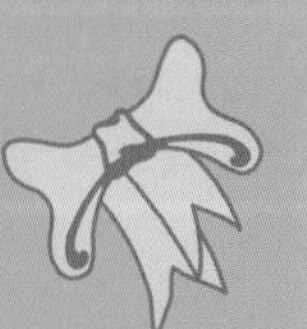

2 Turn the jar upside down and, with the black relief paint, draw the outline of fish and seaweed. Leave to dry.

3 Using the glass paints and brush, colour in the seaweed and fish, blending the paints together. Leave to dry.

4

Fill the jar with water. Add a teaspoon of glitter and a few drops of glycerine.

5

Put a line of glue round the lid and screw it tightly to the top of the jar. Leave it to dry overnight.

Top Tip

Glycerine is great! It makes the water thicker, so that when you shake the jar, the glitter falls to the bottom slowly. You can buy it in the baking department of your supermarket.

Shake the jar and place it upside down to give your fish a glittery sea to swim in.

Foil frame

Make a perfect picture frame from kitchen foil and leftover cardboard. It looks so good, nobody will ever guess you've been recycling!

- ✦ Thick card 120 x 120mm
- ✦ Thin card 120 x 120mm
- ✦ Ruler
- ✦ Scissors
- ✦ Kitchen foil 140 x 140mm
- ✦ PVA glue
- ✦ Old ballpoint pen
- ✦ Small photo

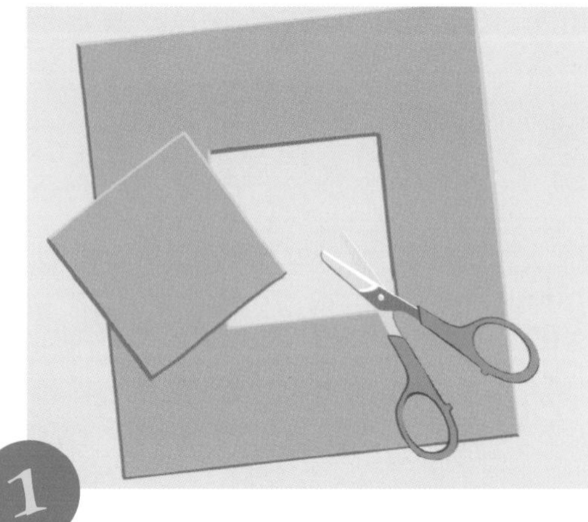

1

Cut out a 50 x 50mm square hole in the middle of the thick card.

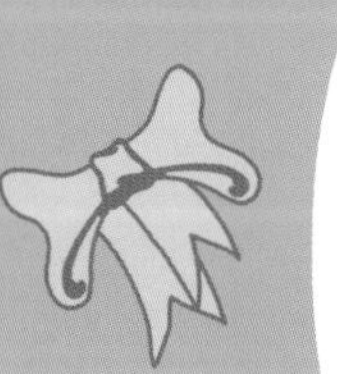

2

Glue the card to the non-shiny side of the foil. Make a hole in the foil and make cuts towards each corner. Fold the triangles you've made onto the back of the frame and glue them down.

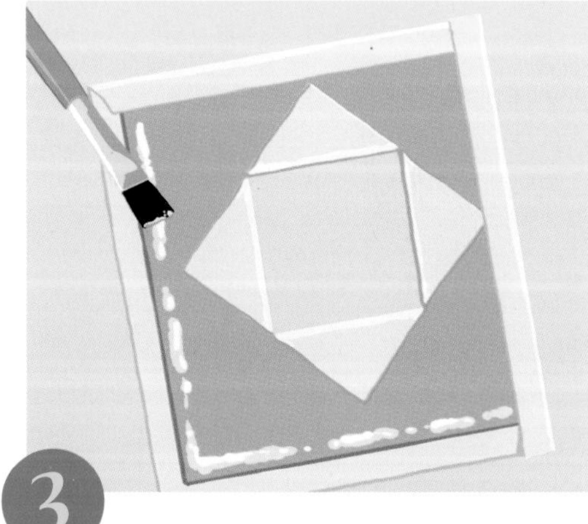

3

Now put a line of glue round the card and glue the four foil edges to it.

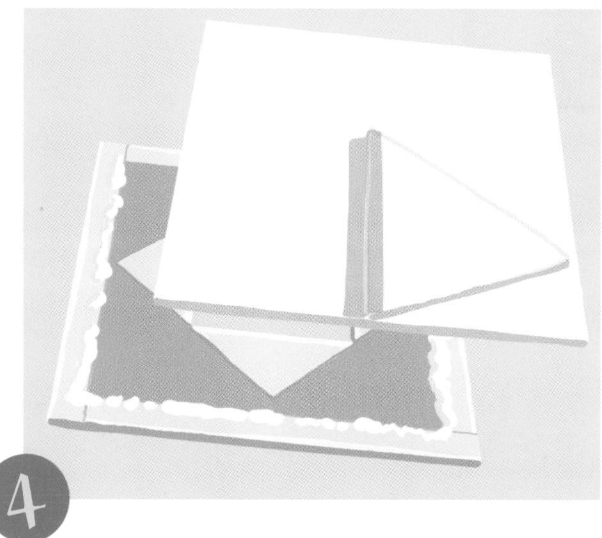

4

Cut out a triangle of card and tape it to the square of thin card as shown, to make a stand. Then glue the two squares of card together round three sides, leaving a slot at the top.

5

Slide a photo into the slot in the frame. Using the empty ballpoint pen, mark your design on the frame. Don't press too hard as you may tear the foil.

Try This!

Heart frame

Cut out a heart-shaped frame and decorate it with heart shapes cut from foil sweet wrappers.

Felt beads

This project is easy-peasy. Just roll up and glue coloured squares of felt, then cut slices to make unusual spiral-patterned beads.

You Will Need

- ✦ Felt squares, 8 x 8cm: yellow, pink and black
- ✦ PVA glue
- ✦ Scissors
- ✦ 2 rubber bands
- ✦ Needle and gold thread
- ✦ 18 small black beads

1 Spread glue thinly onto the black square and stick the pink square on top. Now spread glue onto the pink square and stick the yellow square to it.

2 Spread glue thinly onto the yellow square and roll up the layers to make a swiss-roll shape.

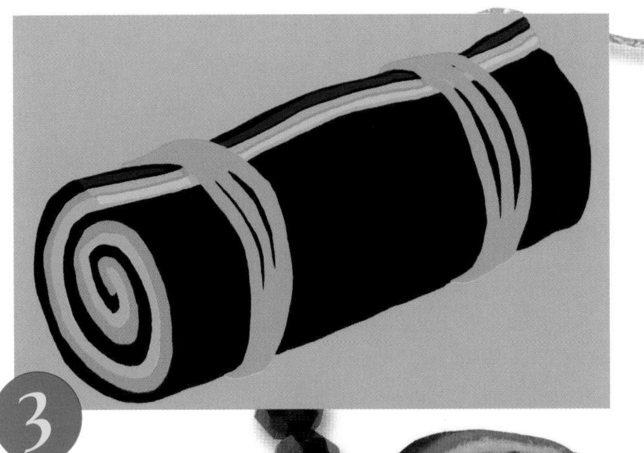

3

Hold the roll in place with a rubber band at each end and leave it to dry.

4

Remove the rubber bands and cut the roll into slices about 12mm wide. Choose the best five beads for your necklace.

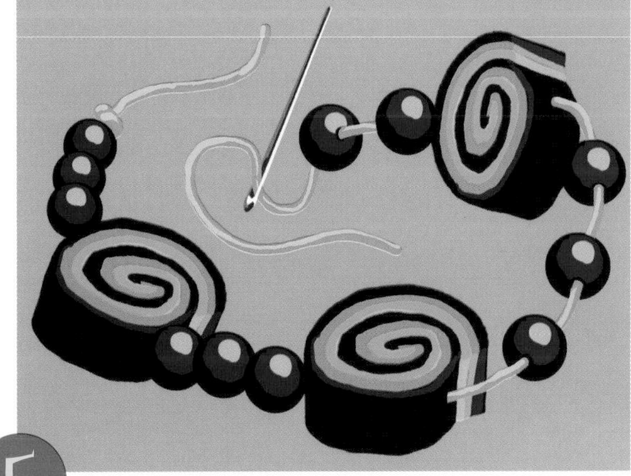

5

Tie a knot in the gold thread about 10cm from the end. Thread on three black beads, then push the needle through the top of one of the felt beads near the join. Thread three more black beads, then the next felt bead. Carry on until you have used all the beads. Tie a knot in the thread and trim the end.

Try This!

Pink pendant

Make a pendant by glueing three felt beads together. Thread beads on as shown. Push the needle through the top of your trio of beads.

Sweetie cushions

These comfy sweetie-shaped cushions look good enough to eat. Make a pile and turn your bedroom into a sweet shop!

You Will Need

For each cushion:

- 1 piece of gold-coloured fabric 50 x 70cm
- 1 piece of coloured netting 50 x 70cm
- Newspaper
- PVA glue
- 2 strong rubber bands
- Cushion filling eg. kapok or synthetic stuffing
- Half metre of gold ribbon

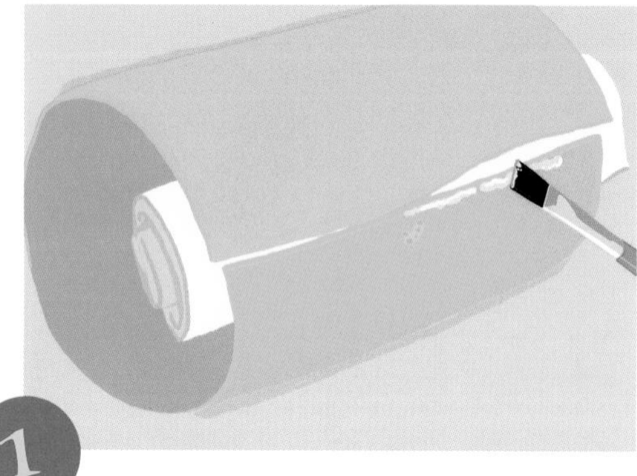

1

Glue the two pieces of fabric together along the longer edges. Stick the short edges together to make a tube. Put newspaper inside to stop the glued seam from sticking to the other side. Leave it to dry.

2

Gather up one end about 14cm from the edge and hold it in place with one of the rubber bands. Wind the band round several times to make it secure.

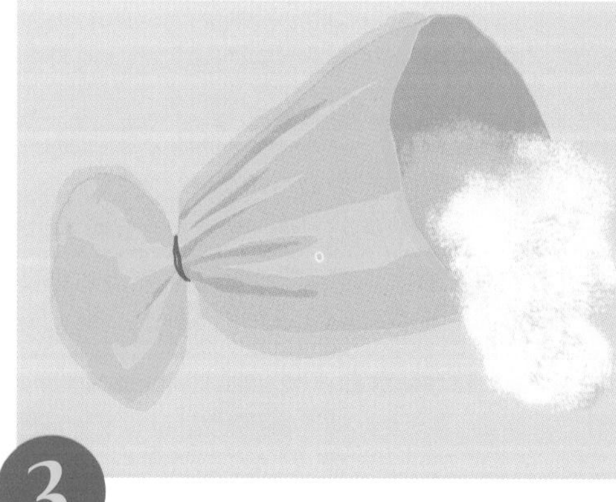

3

Start stuffing the cushion with the filling until it has filled to about 15cm from the top.

4

Close the end with the other rubber band. Fan out the ends of the cushion to make them look like sweet wrappers.

5

Glue some gold ribbon over the rubber bands so that they don't show.

Top Tip

Recycle old cushions by unpicking the seams and re-using the stuffing for your groovy new cushions.

Silhouette hanging

This moonlit woodland scene is made from acetate and cardboard, but it looks just like stained glass!

You Will Need

- Pair of compasses
- 3 x A4 sheets of black card
- Blue acetate film
- Scissors
- Pencil
- PVA glue and brush
- Hole punch

1. Use the compasses to make a 20cm circle on the black card. Draw another circle 2cm in from the first.

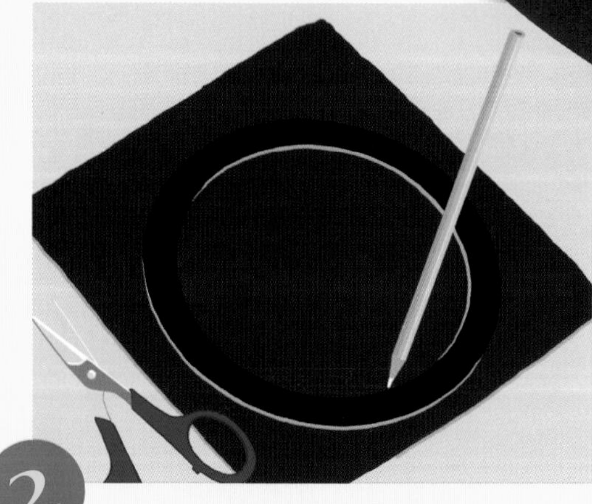

2. Cut out the ring shape, draw round it onto the other piece of card and cut that one out too. Now you have two black rings.

On another piece of black card, draw the outlines of a grassy bank, a tree, two rabbits, a bird and a full moon. Cut them all out.

3

4

Brush glue round one ring and glue the acetate to it, trimming to fit the ring.

5

Glue all the shapes onto the acetate. Cut out a black card tab shape, make a hole in it with the hole punch and glue it to the top of the black ring. Glue the other black ring on top of the acetate.

Top Tip

Thread some cord through the tab and hang your picture by a window. The sun will shine through it and really make it glow.

Funky friendship bracelet

Tell your best buddy what you think of them with this brilliant friendship bracelet.

You Will Need

- ✦ 2 mauve, 1 pink and 1 purple strand each 50cms long
- ✦ 1 large bead and 4 medium-sized beads

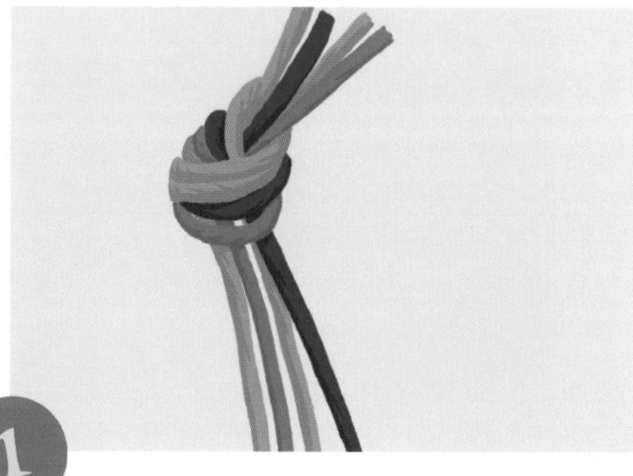

1 Take the four strands and knot them together 3cms from one end.

2 Thread the large bead on and push it up as far as the knot.

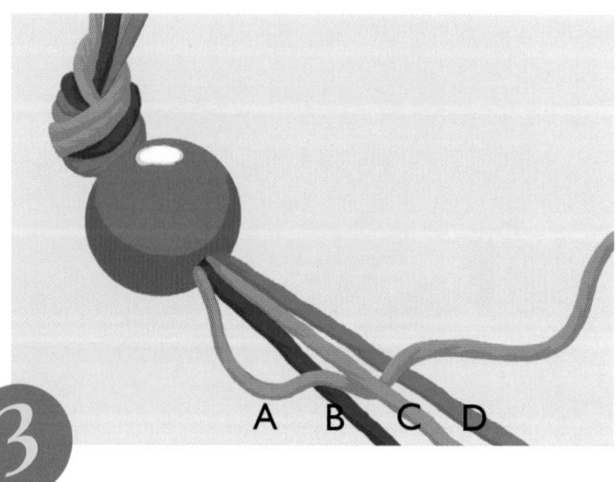

3 Spread out the four strands so that the 2 mauve strands are first and third from the left. Put A over B, under C and over D. Pull A gently to tighten the weave.

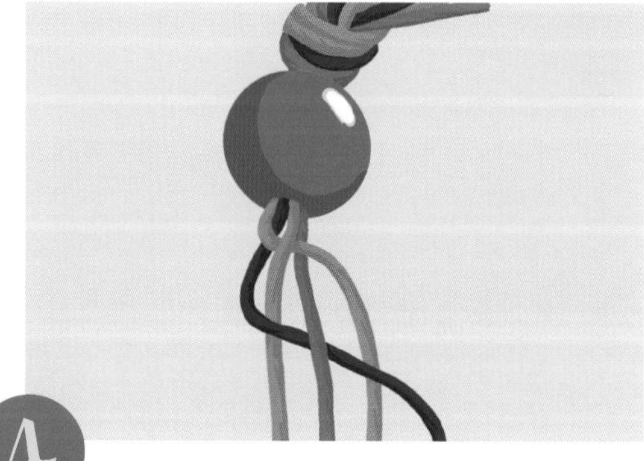

4 Keep on threading the left-hand thread to the right, working over, under, over, under. Pull gently to tighten before starting on the next left-hand thread.

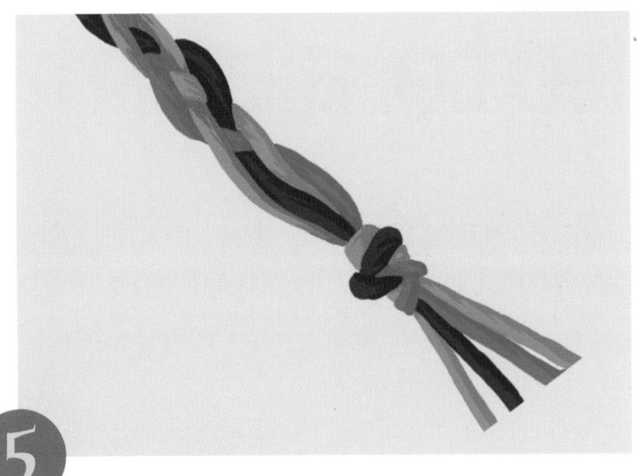

5

Continue threading until you are about 8cms from the end, then tie the knotted strands into a knot, leaving the ends loose.

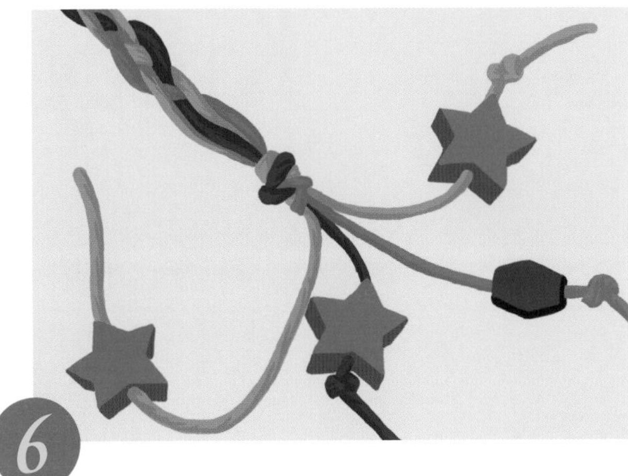

6

Thread a medium-sized bead onto each of the four loose strands and tie a knot to keep in place.

Try This!

Keyring

You can use the same weaving method to make other gifts. This keyring was made with purple and orange strands threaded with pink beads.

Kitty photo album

Making pictures from different shapes and colours of paper is called collage. This collage photo album makes a purr-fect present for your favourite cat lover!

You Will Need

- 6 sheets A4 coloured card
- Scraps of card in orange, white, pink, green, black, and blue
- Hole punch
- Zig-zag scissors
- PVA glue
- 1m length of green cord

1. Pile together the six sheets of coloured card with cover sheet on top. Punch two holes on the left-hand side.

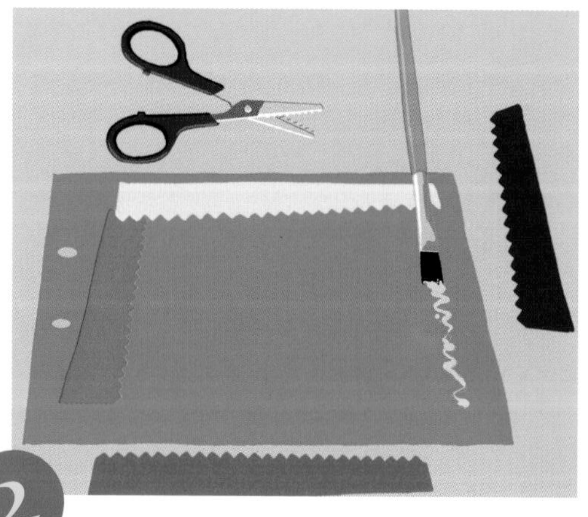

2. Cut a strip each from the card scraps, using the zig-zag scissors. Arrange them to make a border on the cover and glue in place.

3. Draw and cut out a large cat face from orange card. Stick it on the cover, overlapping the borders as shown.

4

Draw and cut out the cat's features: oval white eyes with green and black pupils, a pink nose, mouth and ears, and black whiskers. Arrange these on the face and glue them in place.

5

Thread the length of cord through the holes, starting from the back and including all the pages. Tie in a bow at the front. Knot the ends of the cord to stop them from fraying.

Secret book box

Fed up with sneaky sisters or beastly brothers pinching your treasures? This clever box disguised as a book will really fool them!

You Will Need

- Empty cereal box
- A4 sheet of white card
- Pencil and ruler
- PVA glue
- 0.75m length of 20mm yellow ribbon
- A3 sheet of light blue funky foam
- A4 sheet of dark blue funky foam

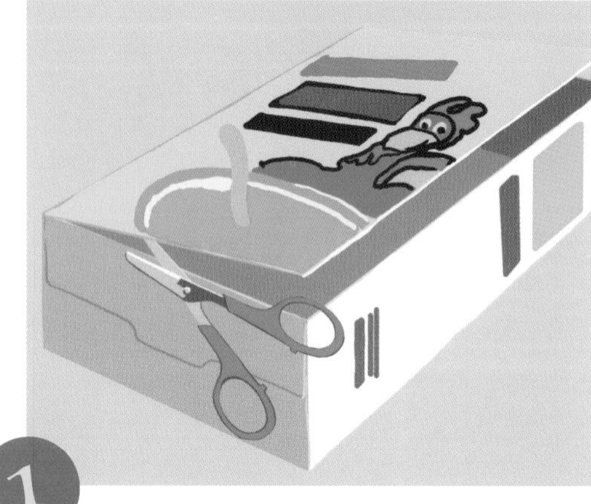

1. Cut the front of the empty box round three sides. Leave the left side uncut so it makes a flap.

2. Draw straight lines on the white card along the longer side. Using the box as a guide, cut out pieces of the lined card to fit on the top, bottom and side of the box. Glue them in place.

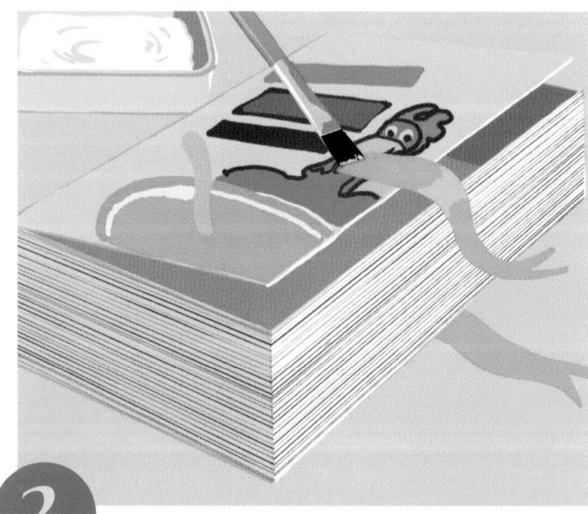

3. Cut the ribbon in half and glue one piece to the back of the box and the other to the front flap, halfway down.

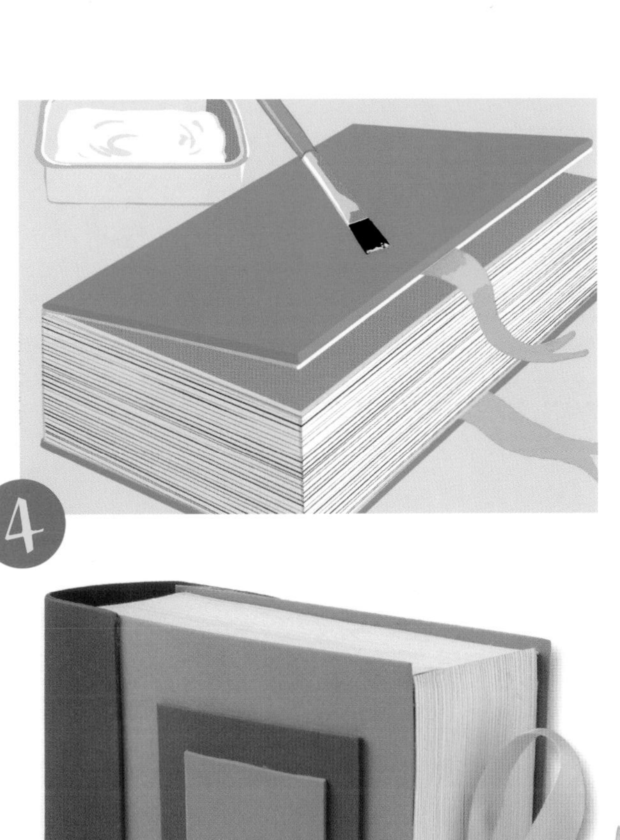

4

◂ Using the box as a guide, cut two pieces of light blue funky foam, each a few mm bigger than the box on all sides. Glue one piece to the front flap and the other to the back.

5

Cut a piece of dark blue foam the same height as the box and 150mm wide. Glue in place on the side of the box to make the spine of the book. Cut small pieces of funky foam to decorate the front and spine of the book.

Top Tip

Use a marker pen to give your book a boring title so that nobody will open it – such as 'How to Tidy Your Bedroom' by A. Mum.

Flowery earrings

It's really easy to make jewellery with oven-bake clay and it comes in so many colours you'll never run out of ideas.

You Will Need

- Oven-bake clay: red, yellow, blue
- Rolling pin
- Plastic sheet or tablecloth
- Plastic knife
- Earring backs
- All-purpose glue

1 Spread out a plastic sheet or old tablecloth to work on. Work the clay in your hands to warm it. Roll out the blue clay to about 1-2mm.

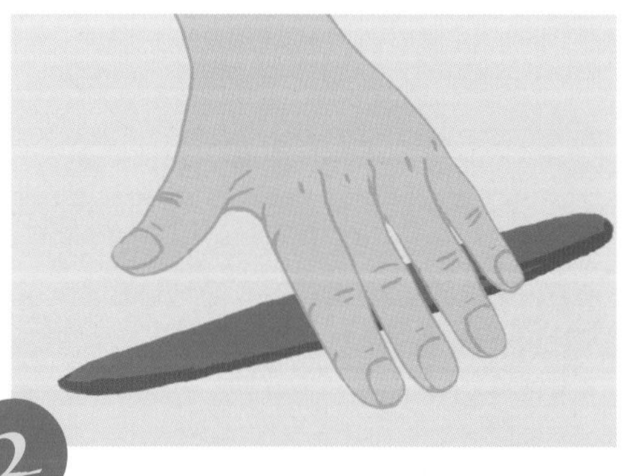

2 Take half the piece of red clay and roll it into a sausage about 6-7mm in diameter.

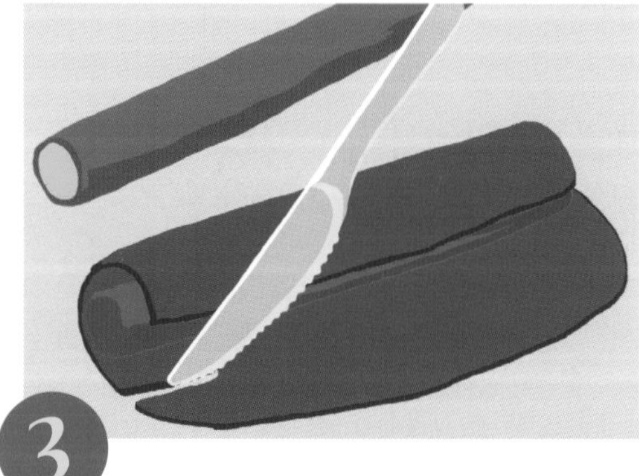

3 Put the red sausage on the blue piece and roll them up together. Now make a red sausage with a yellow middle in the same way.

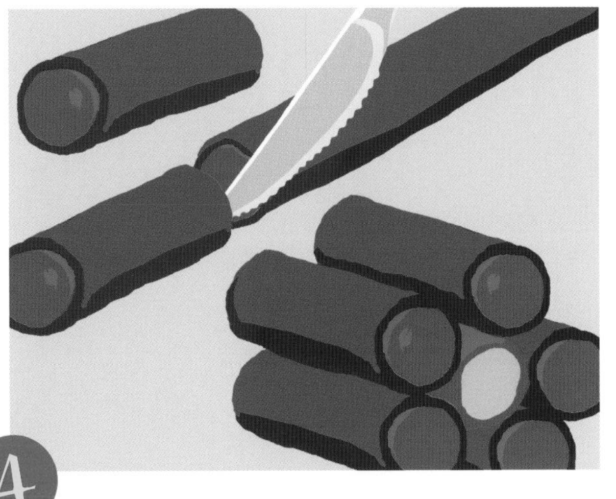

4

Cut the blue sausage into five equal lengths, and cut two equal lengths of the red sausage. Arrange them in a flower shape as shown.

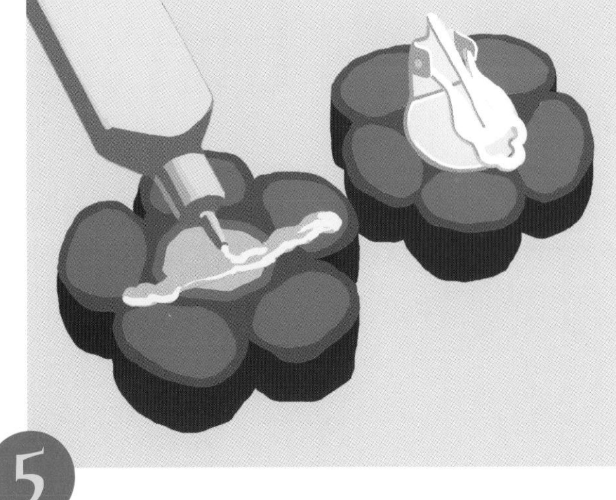

5

Use the plastic knife to slice the shape into two pieces. Bake them in the oven following the maker's instructions. Leave them to cool, then glue the earring backs on.

Pretty pendants

Once you get the hang of handling the clay, you can create all kinds of designs - let your imagination run wild! These drop earrings were made with leftovers from the main project.

Candy mirror

This is a cunning way to make a boring old mirror more exciting. Instead of sweets, you could use beads, sequins or buttons.

You Will Need

- Bag of small sweets
- Spray varnish
- Cocktail sticks and blob of modelling clay
- PVA glue and brush
- Old mirror

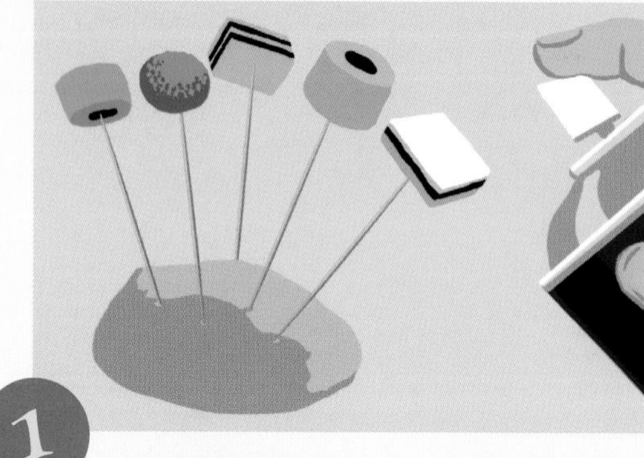

1 Spear the sweets on cocktail sticks stuck in clay. Get an adult to spray them with varnish.

2 When the varnish is dry, brush glue onto the backs of the sweets and stick them in a border all the way round the mirror.

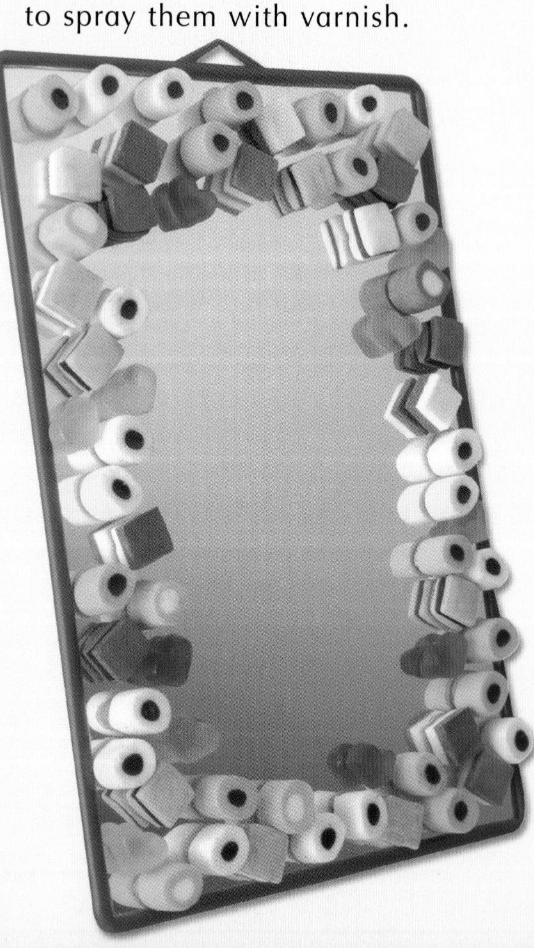

MODELLING

Dog and kennel

Make a dotty dalmatian from oven-bake clay; then turn an old juice carton into a cosy kennel for him to curl up in.

You Will Need

- ✦ Juice or milk carton
- ✦ Scissors
- ✦ Paintbrush
- ✦ Paints: yellow, red, green
- ✦ Oven bake clay: Black, white, red

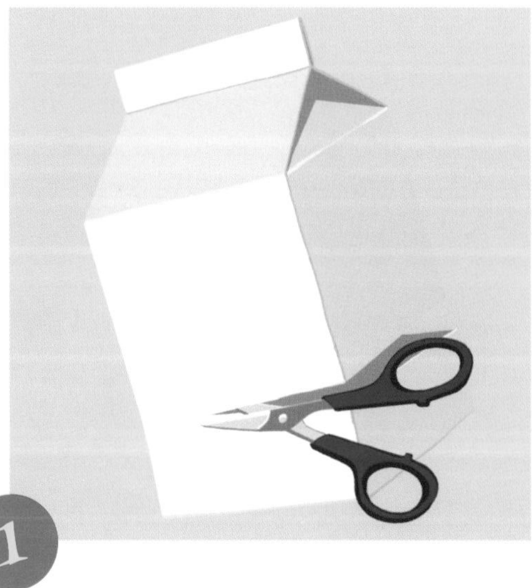

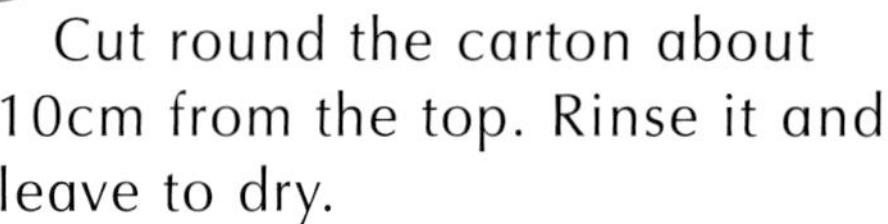

1 Cut round the carton about 10cm from the top. Rinse it and leave to dry.

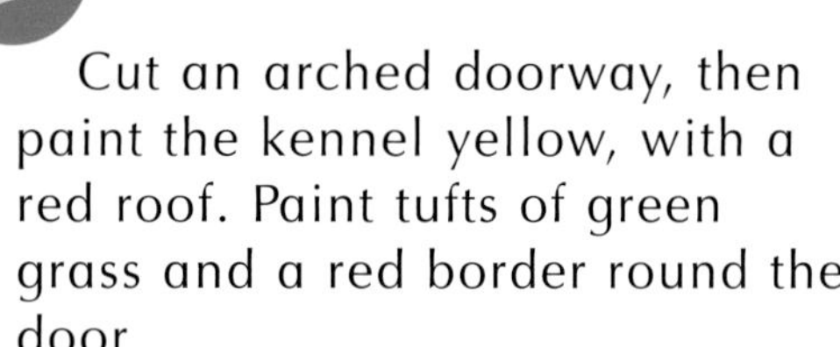

2 Cut an arched doorway, then paint the kennel yellow, with a red roof. Paint tufts of green grass and a red border round the door.

Try This!

Dog's dinner

Complete the scene by making your pooch a juicy bone with white clay and a doggy bowl with the red clay.

3

◂ Use the white clay to make the head and body shapes of the dog. Push the head onto the body, making sure it is firmly attached.

4

Make one white and one black ear, and a black patch for the forehead. Now make little sausage shapes for the legs and tail, and add all of them to your model.

5

Stick on black spots and a round nose, one black eye and one with a black spot in the middle of a white spot. Use red for the collar and tongue. Bake your model according to manufacturer's instructions.

Clay egg cup

This big-footed egg cup is brilliant. Paint a funny face on your boiled egg and make breakfast time really egg-citing!

You Will Need

- 200g air- drying clay
- Plastic knife
- Egg
- Acrylic paints: blue, red, black
- Paintbrush

1

Set a quarter of the clay to one side. Roll the remaining clay into a ball and use your thumbs to work it into a bowl shape. Check the bowl with an egg, working on the shape until the egg sits snugly in the hollow.

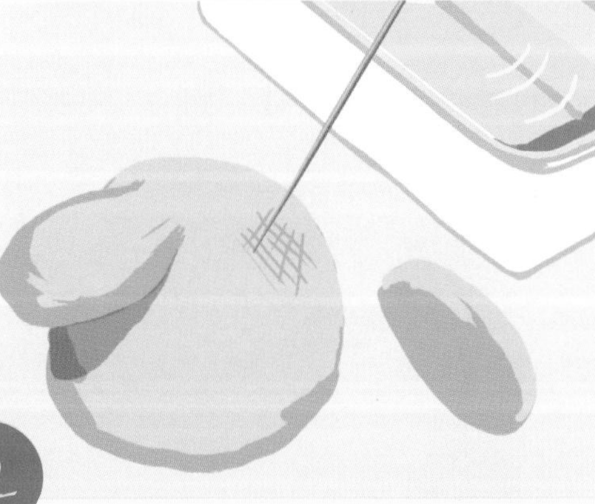

2

Divide the remaining clay into two equal pieces. Make a fat foot shape out of each and fix them to the base of the bowl. Score the bowl with a cocktail stick and wet each piece to help them stick.

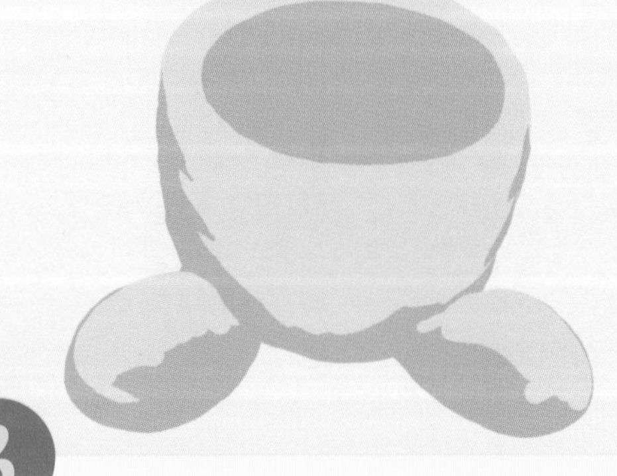

3

Turn the model the right way up and adjust the feet until the model stands on a surface without wobbling. Leave to dry overnight.

4 Paint the bowl of the egg cup blue. Paint red socks and black shoes, adding a black line across the socks to make a bar.

Try This!

Trendy trainers

Use a cocktail stick to add details to the jeans and small flattened pieces of clay to make tongues for trainers. Paint the jeans red and blue and the trainers silver with black laces and toes.

Top Tip

Don't put your egg cup in the dishwasher. Wash it quickly and carefully by hand to keep it looking good as new.

Flying bird mobile

Turn your bedroom into a tropical bird paradise with a colourful mobile. Invisible thread makes it look as if the birds are really flying!

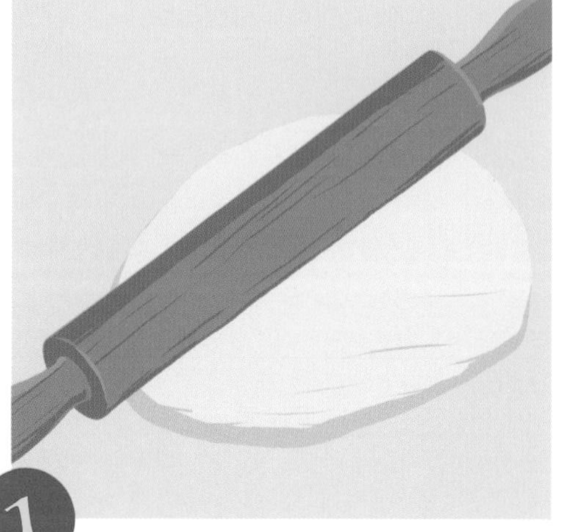

1 Roll out the air-drying clay to about ½ cm thick.

You Will Need

- Pack of air-drying clay
- Rolling pin
- Paper
- Plastic knife
- Old ball-point pen
- Set of paints, including gold
- Paintbrush
- 5 coloured feathers
- Sequins
- Coloured and invisible thread
- 50cm wire and pliers

2 Trace the bird template on p223 onto a piece of paper and cut it out. Put it on the clay and cut round it with a plastic knife. Repeat until you have made five birds. Use an old pen to make a hole at the top of each bird. Leave to dry.

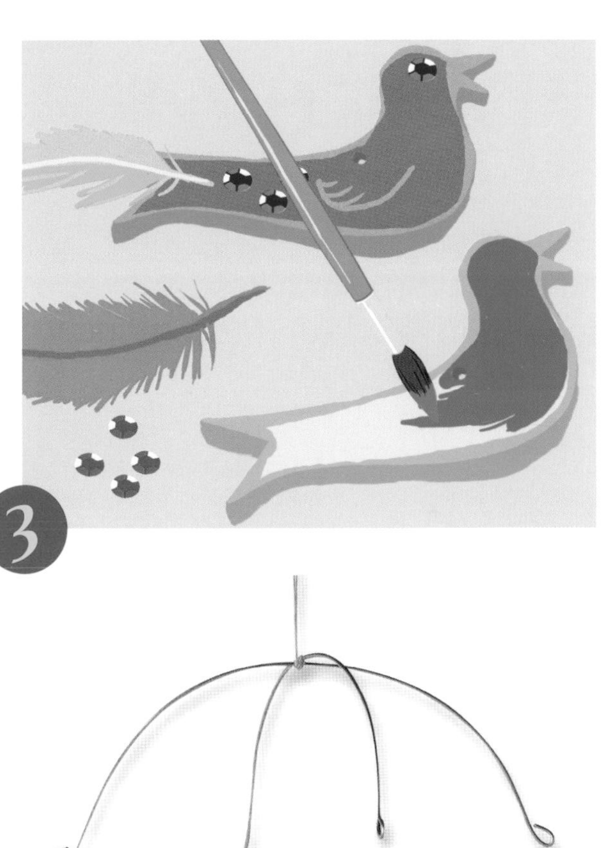

3

Decorate the birds in acrylic paints, then outline them gold paint and glue on sequins. Glue a feather to each tail.

4

Get an adult to help with this. Cut two pieces of wire 25cm long, and use pliers to make small hooks at the ends. Bend the wires into semicircles. Tie the wires together with a long piece of coloured thread.

5

Use invisible thread to attach a bird to each hook. Hang the fifth bird from where the two wires join at the centre.

Mosaic plate

Make your very own Roman mosaic. Simply make tiles from clay and get designing! Create a spiral like this, or copy a simple drawing you have made.

You Will Need

- Old dinner plate
- Oven-bake clay: white, orange, red, green, blue
- Plaster of Paris
- Butter knife
- Rolling pin
- Plate-hanging hook

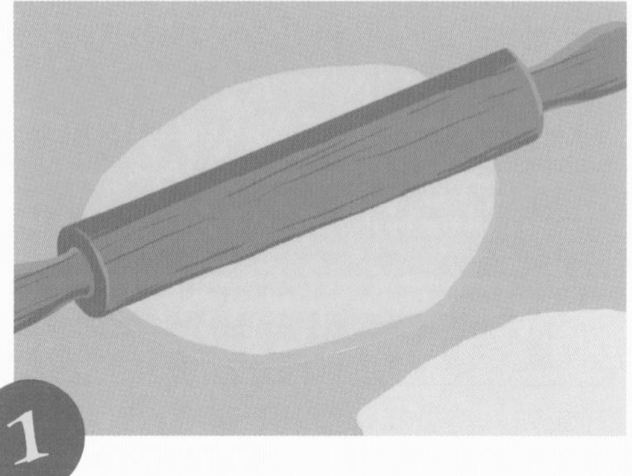

1 Roll out each colour of clay to about ½ cm thick.

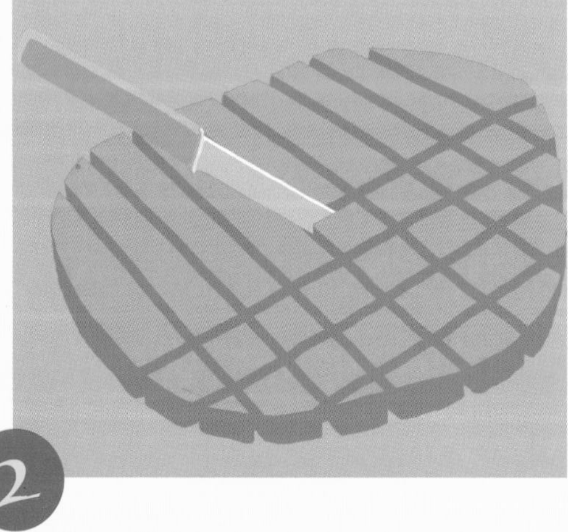

2 Cut all the clay layers into 5mm squares. Ask an adult to put the squares in the oven and bake them according to the maker's instructions.

3 Mix some plaster of Paris with water in a plastic bowl and smear it all over the plate. Lay out the tiles on a work surface in a spiral pattern.

4

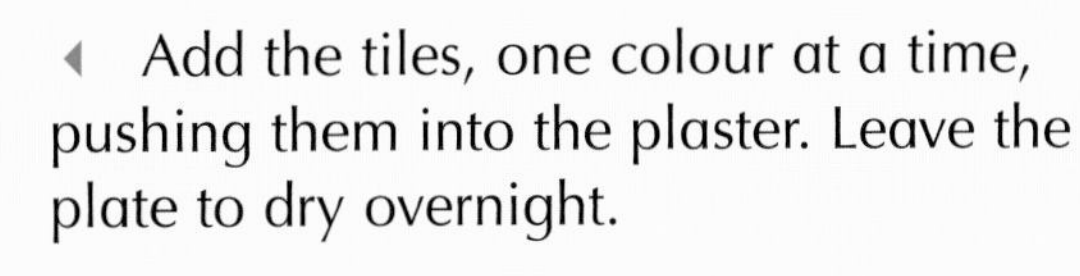
Add the tiles, one colour at a time, pushing them into the plaster. Leave the plate to dry overnight.

Wipe the plate with a damp cloth to remove any extra bits of plaster.

Why not hang your plate on the wall for everyone to admire? You can buy plate hanging hooks in DIY stores.

Top Tip

Apply a thin coat of varnish to your plate to make it extra long-lasting.

Brilliant beads

These beads are made from three different colours of clay, but if you only have one colour simply make the beads and, when they are dry, paint them instead.

You Will Need

- Air-drying clay: green, yellow, turquoise
- Darning needle
- 15 cocktail sticks
- Thin elastic thread

1 Roll the three colours of clay into sausages and put them side by side. Use a plastic knife to cut sections of about the same size through all three lengths together.

Make sure you make all the balls the same size!

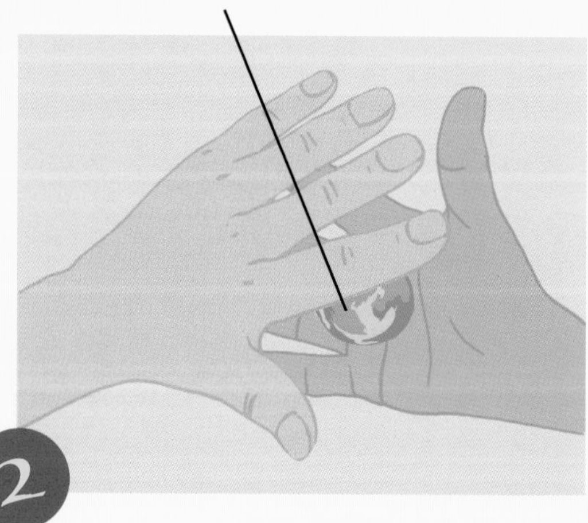

2 Take a section and roll it into a ball between your palms until the colours are mixed together. Repeat until you have made about 15 balls.

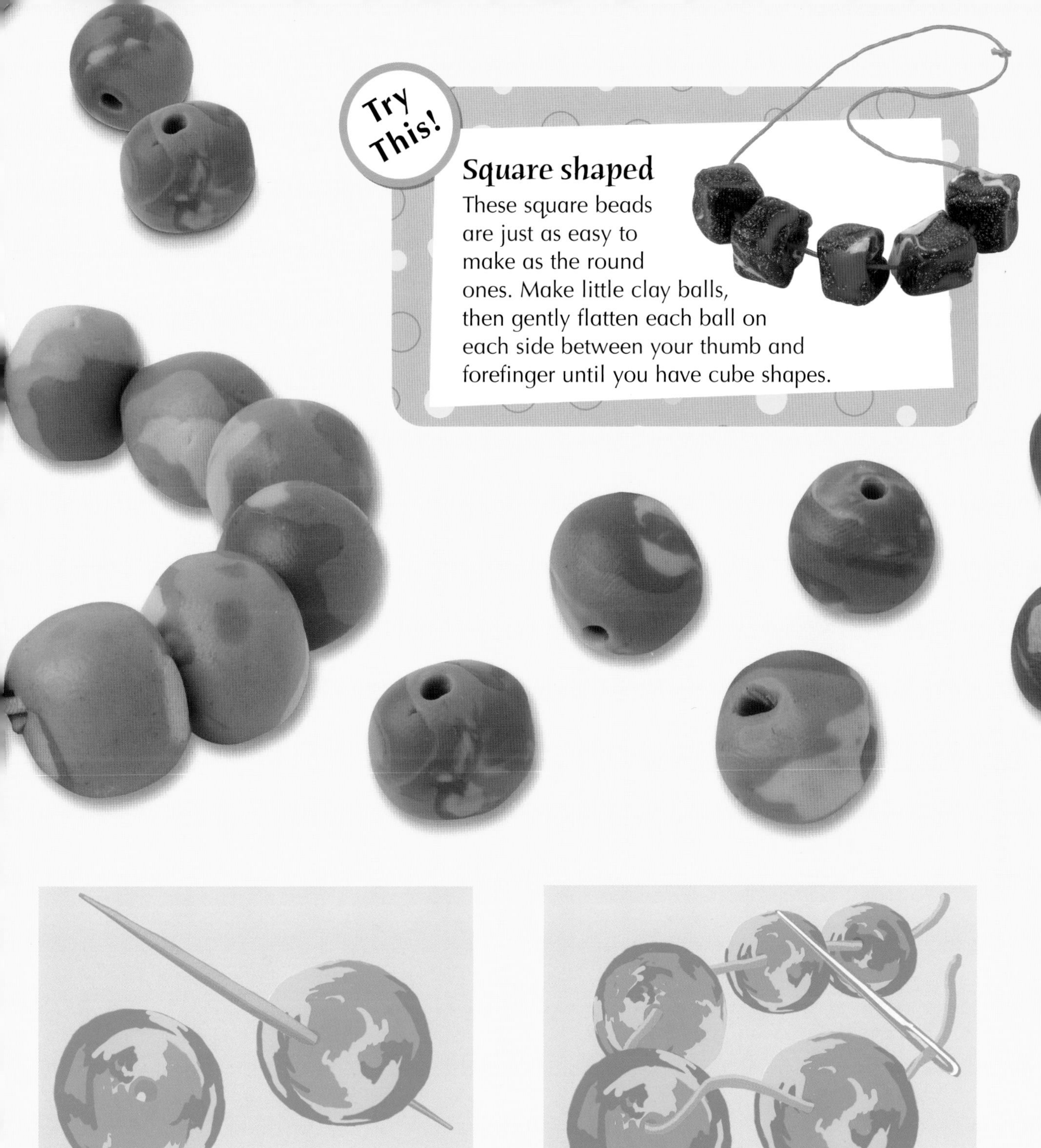

Try This!

Square shaped

These square beads are just as easy to make as the round ones. Make little clay balls, then gently flatten each ball on each side between your thumb and forefinger until you have cube shapes.

3

Push a cocktail stick through the middle of each ball. Balance the sticks across the top of a mug, so that the beads are suspended in the air, and leave them to dry. They will be ready in about 24 hours.

4

Use a darning needle to thread the beads onto thin elastic until you have enough to go around your wrist comfortably. Knot the two ends of elastic together and trim the ends.

Papier mâché CD holder

Cereal bar boxes are perfect to make this groovy CD holder, so get munching!

You Will Need

- 4 identical empty cardboard packets
- Scissors
- PVA glue
- Masking tape
- Thick card
- Torn newspaper pieces
- Paints: white, silver
- Brush
- 3 old CDs

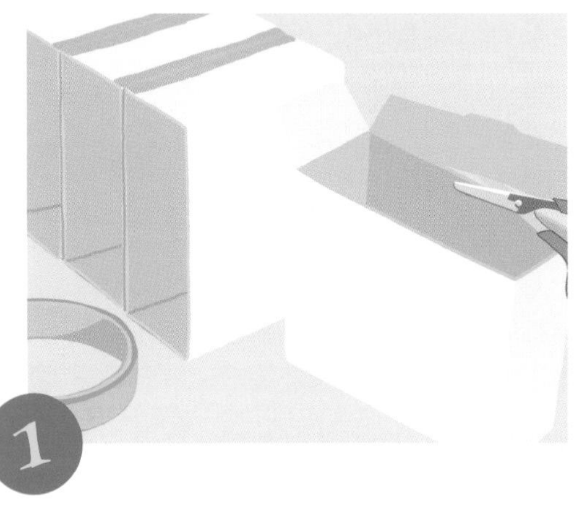

1 Cut the lids off all the boxes. Glue the boxes in a row and add masking tape along the joins.

2 Cut out two squares of thick card the same size as the box sides, and glue one to each end of the boxes.

3 Make papier mâché mix following the recipe on p6. Apply a layer of newspaper all over the outside and round the edges of the boxes.

4

When the papier mâché is dry, paint the boxes white all over. Leave to dry.

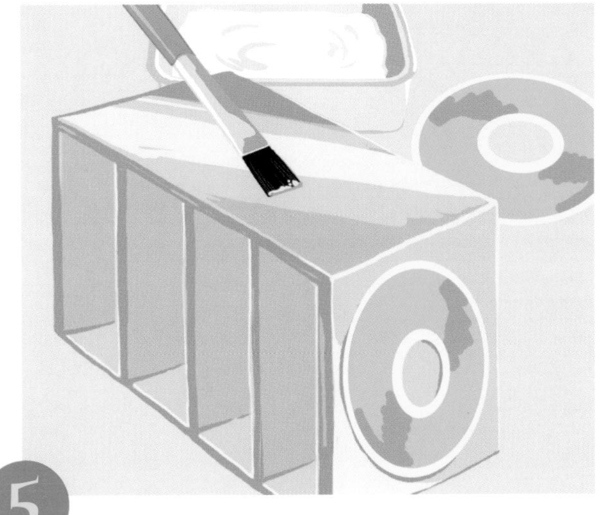

5

Paint the outside silver. When it is dry, glue a CD on each end and on the top.

Scented hangings

Hang these fragrant little butterflies in your wardrobe and your clothes will always smell fresh. They make great gifts, too!

You Will Need

- Salt dough mixture (see p 7)
- Butterfly-shaped cookie cutter
- Acrylic paints
- Ribbon
- Cocktail stick
- Rolling pin
- Baking sheet
- Lavender essential oil

1 Make up the salt dough, using the recipe on p7. Roll it out to a thickness of about 2cm.

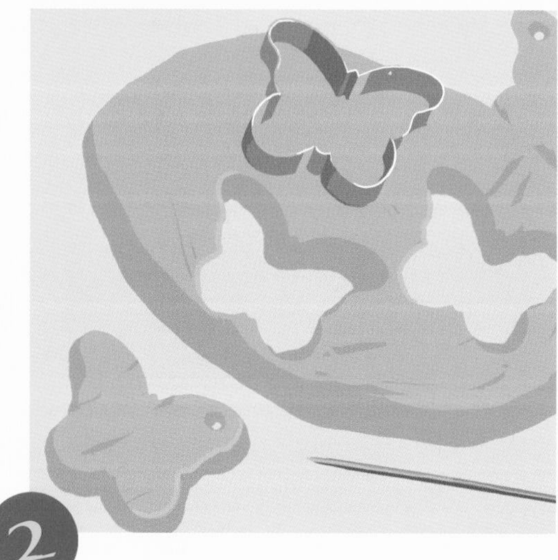

2 Use a cookie cutter to cut shapes out of the dough. Make a hole at the top of each shape with the cocktail stick.

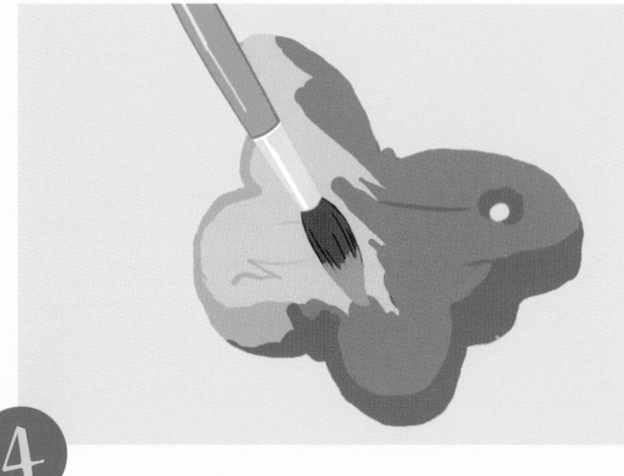

3

Get an adult to help here. Put the shapes on a baking sheet and bake as in the recipe on p7. Leave to cool.

4

Paint the shapes, leaving a small square on the back unpainted.

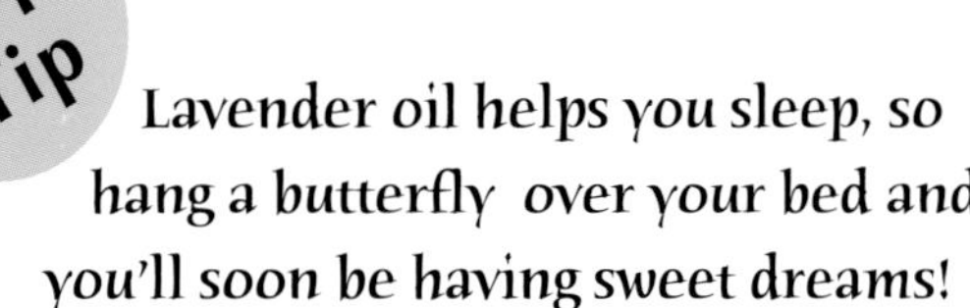

Top Tip

Lavender oil helps you sleep, so hang a butterfly over your bed and you'll soon be having sweet dreams!

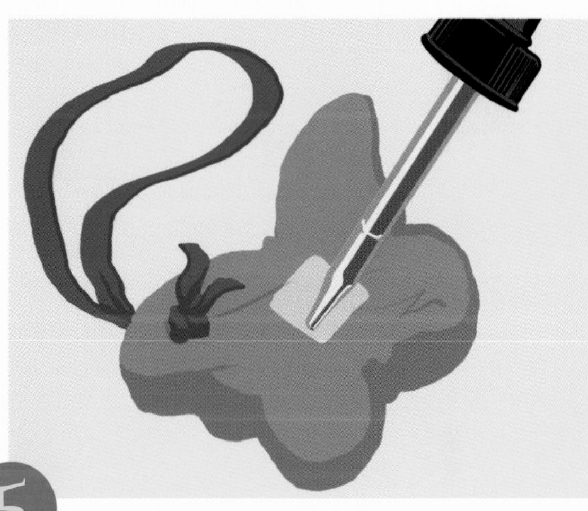

5

Add a few drops of lavender essential oil to the unpainted area. Thread a ribbon through the hole and knot it at the back.

Try This!

Valentine's gift

Heart-shaped hangings make a great Valentine's day gift for a special friend!

Mini farmyard

Make your own farmyard scene of cute sheep and clucking chickens with oven-drying clay. Get an adult to help you bake them.

You Will Need

- Oven-drying clay: brown, red, yellow, white, black, green

1

For the hens, mould the brown clay into simple croissant shapes.

2

Stick a lump of red at one end for the comb, and a tiny red one underneath for the wattle. Add a yellow beak.

3

Add small black blobs for eyes. Mount the hen on a flattened green blob and push it down well.

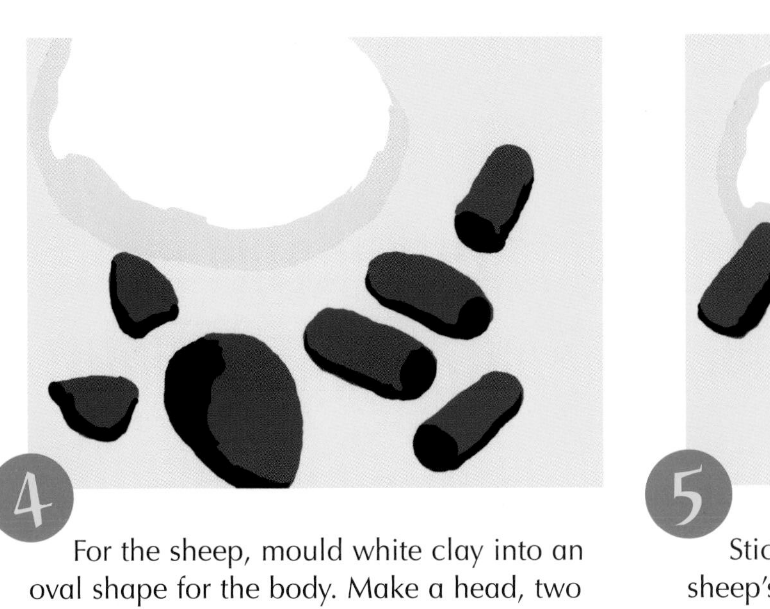

4

For the sheep, mould white clay into an oval shape for the body. Make a head, two ears and four legs out of the black clay.

5

Stick the head, ears and legs to the sheep's body. Wet the clay slightly to make it stick better. Bake all the animals in the oven, following the manufacturer's instructions.

Papier mâché bowl

Balloons are great for making bowls – after the papier mâché dries, simply pop the balloon to leave a perfect bowl shape!

1

Blow up the balloon. Make the papier mâché mix using the recipe on p7. Paste a layer of newspaper strips halfway up the balloon. Repeat with three more layers.

You Will Need

- Balloon
- Torn newspaper pieces
- PVA glue and water
- Scissors
- Masking tape
- Round cheese spread box lid
- White emulsion paint and brush
- Ruler and pencil
- Set of acrylic paints
- Water-based varnish and brush

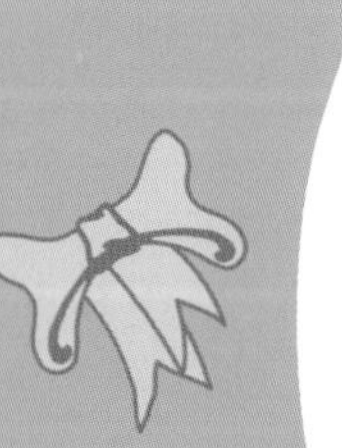

2

When it is dry, pop the balloon and remove it. Trim the edges of the bowl by cutting round the rim.

3

Sit the bowl in the cheese lid and tape them together. Paste two more layers of papier mâché over the whole model and leave it to dry.

4

Paint the pot all over, including the inside, with a coat of white emulsion. Leave to dry. Hold the ruler up beside the pot and mark two straight lines of dots round the bowl. Join the dots to make lines.

5

Paint on a stripey pattern in bright colours and leave to dry. Add spots, triangles and black outlines. Leave to dry then add a thin coat of varnish to make the bowl tough and shiny.

Copy this colourful tribal design or make up a pattern of your own.

Top Tip

It's important to leave papier mâché to dry before you pop the balloon or start painting. If it is still soft and damp, you could easily put your finger through it!

Farmyard barn

Don't forget to save all your old cardboard boxes. You can use them to make this great barn for your farmyard toys.

You Will Need

- Plain and corrugated cardboard
- Scissors
- Pencil and ruler
- Brush and PVA glue
- Green and pink tissue paper
- Paints: cream, brown, dark brown, orange

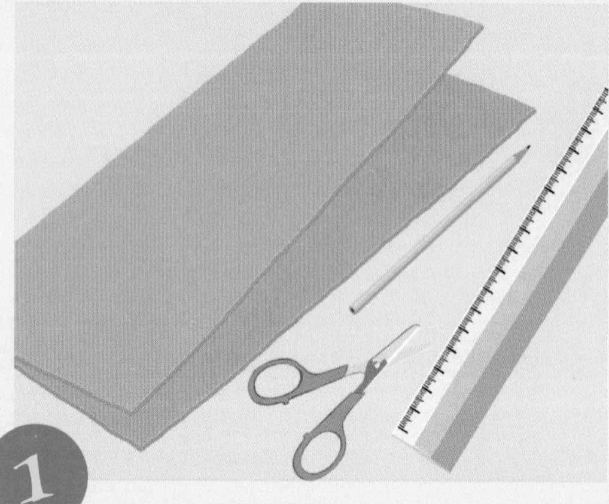

1 Cut out two pieces of cardboard measuring 25 x 10cm. These will be the base and back of the barn.

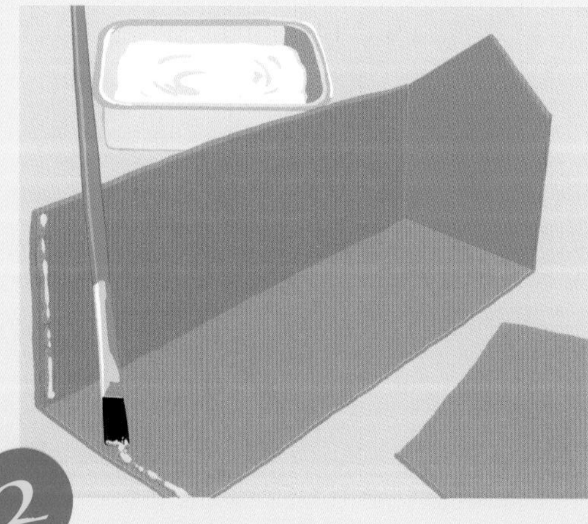

2 Now cut two more rectangles measuring 10 x 15cm. Put them on top of one another and cut the corners off to make a roof shape. Glue all four pieces together and leave to dry.

3 Cut three rectangles measuring 7 x 10cm to make the stalls. Glue them in place and leave to dry.

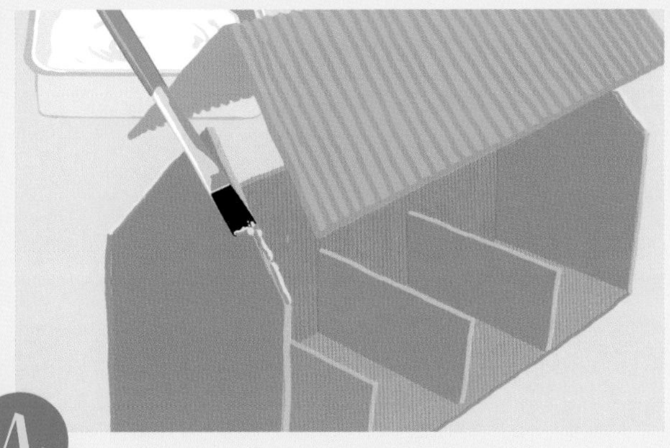

4

Cut a rectangle measuring 20 x 25cm from the corrugated card. Make a crease by folding in half lengthways, then put it on top of the barn and glue it in place.

5

Paint the roof brown and the rest of the barn creamy white. Put windows and a chicken on the side in dark brown. Paint the floor brown and add some straw in orange.

Top Tip

Corrugated cardboard is often used to package furniture or electrical goods, so keep a lookout for it.

6

When the paint has dried, make flowers and leaves by scrunching up scraps of tissue paper and glueing them to the side of the barn.

Photo-frame fridge magnet

This fridge magnet is designed to look like a dog's collar. It's perfect for showing off a photo of your favourite pooch!

You Will Need

- Oven bake clay: red, yellow
- Pencil
- PVA glue
- Small magnet
- A5 piece of card

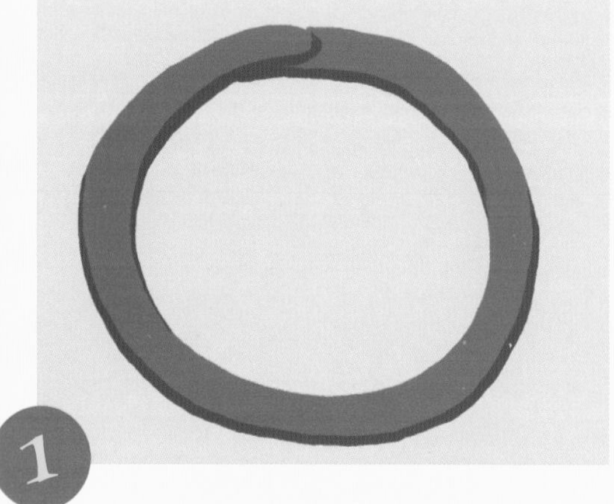

1

Roll out a piece of red clay into a sausage shape about 2cm thick and 20cm long Make the shape into a circle, overlapping the edges and pressing them together gently with your fingers.

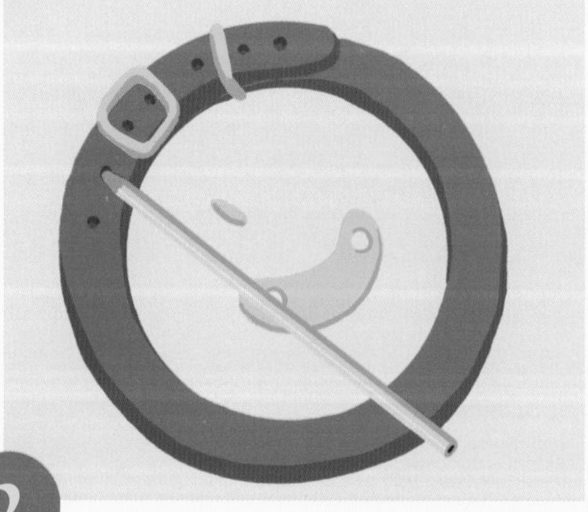

2

Add a buckle and a name tag in yellow clay. Use a pencil to make holes in the collar. Put the shape on a baking tray and bake according to manufacturer's instructions.

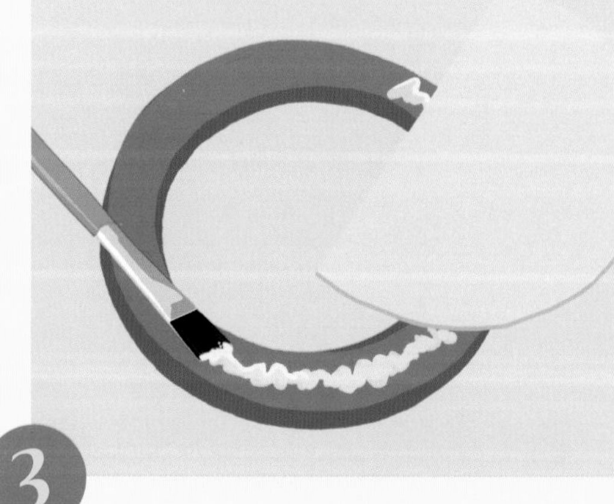

3

Cut a circle of card slightly smaller than the frame. Cut off the top third of the circle. Brush glue round the frame and stick the card to it to make a pocket.

4

Trim your dog photo so that it will fit in the frame. Slip it into the pocket.

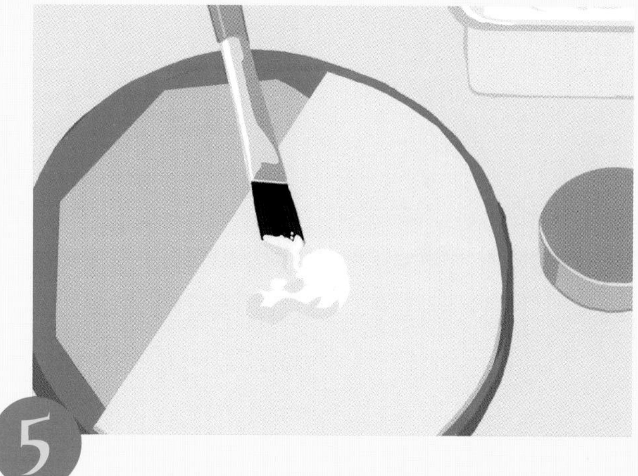

5

Glue a magnet onto the back of the frame and leave it to dry.

Try This!

You've been framed!

Design a frame and put a picture of yourself in it. Now all you need to do is find someone who'd like to see your smiling face on their fridge every day!

Flowerpot pups

Get cracking with air-drying clay to make this doggy flowerpot. With his huge eyes and flappy tongue, he looks barking mad!

You Will Need

- Flowerpot, 90mm diameter
- Air-drying clay
- Cocktail stick
- Plastic knife
- Brown acrylic paint and paint brush
- Tube of gold paint

1

Roll a ball of clay about 4cms in diameter. Cut into the ball and pull it gently apart to make the dog's jowls. Wet one side with your fingers and fix to the centre of the pot. Prick each side with a cocktail stick.

Top Tip

Speed up the drying process by putting your pot in a warm, dry place, such as the airing cupboard.

2

Roll a small ball of clay for the nose and stick it on top of the jowls. Make holes in it for nostrils. Stick on a tongue shape and two round eyes, with smaller balls for the eyeballs.

3

For the ears, make 2 tapered ovals about 8cm long. Use the knife to dab marks all over them. Attach them on each side by wetting and smoothing them onto the surface, leaving the loose ends to hang over the side. Leave to dry overnight.

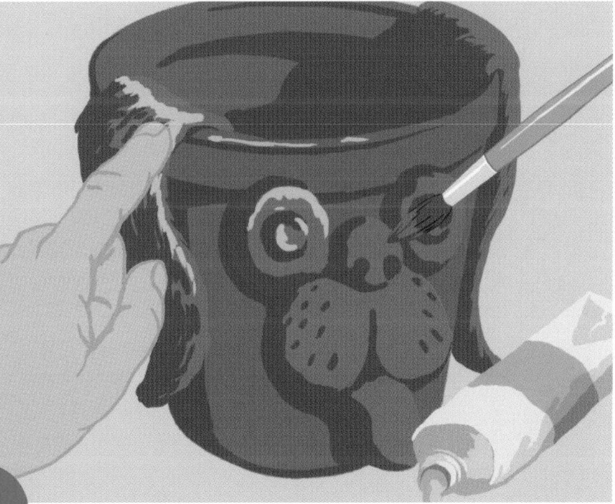

4

Paint the pot all over with the brown acrylic paint. Leave to dry. Use your finger to rub small amounts of gold paint over the pot, so it gleams in the light.

Try This!

Family of pots

Create a whole family of different dog pots! This miniature pup is painted red and was made with a 50mm pot.

Slithery snail pots

These cute snails look great and they have a useful secret – you can hide your tiny treasures under their shell!

You Will Need

- 150g air-drying clay
- Plastic knife
- Purple pipe cleaner
- Cocktail stick
- Acrylic paints: red, blue, yellow, purple, black, white
- Paintbrush

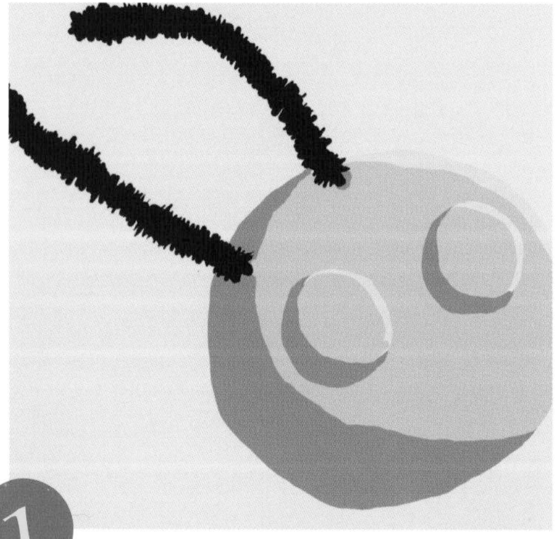

1

Cut the clay in half. From one half take enough to roll a 20mm ball of clay and two tiny balls. Stick the two tiny balls on the 20mm ball for the eyes, flattening them as you fix them on. Cut two pieces of pipe cleaner and poke them into the head.

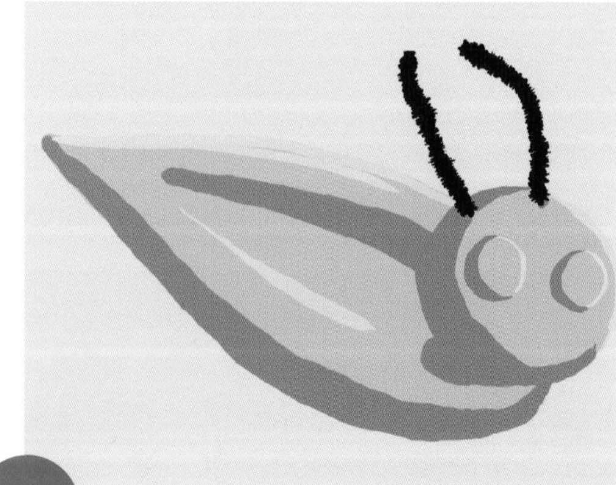

2

With the rest of the clay from the first half, make a tapered oval shape. Use your thumbs to indent it a little in the middle. Stick the head to the untapered end.

3

Roll the other half of clay into a ball. Use your thumbs to shape the ball into a hollow snail's shell shape. Make sure the shape fits the base of your model. Add a spiral on each side using the cocktail stick. Leave all the pieces to dry overnight.

4

Paint the head purple, the eyes white and the base blue.

Spotty grasshopper

For a grasshopper pot, make a long base and lid and push green pipe-cleaner legs into the base. Paint the pot bright green all over and add red spots.

5

Paint the shell yellow and red and pick out the spiral with black paint. Using the black paint, add a smiley mouth and pupils to the eyes.

Lighthouse

Ahoy there, landlubbers! To make this model lighthouse project even easier, you can make it with ready-mixed filler – buy it in a DIY shop.

You Will Need

- 500g plaster of Paris
- Water
- Shoe box lid
- Yogurt pot
- Sticky tape
- Plastic knife
- Old plastic mixing container
- About 20 small pebbles
- Air-drying clay
- Acrylic paints: blue, white, green, brown, black
- All-purpose glue

1. Turn the yogurt pot upside down and tape it to the upturned lid.

Make the surface rough so it looks like a choppy sea.

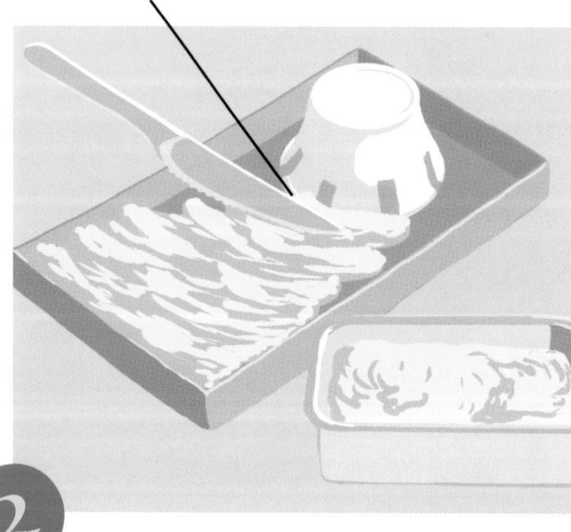

2. Mix the plaster of Paris with water in a plastic container until it is thick and sticky. Spread the mixture all over the base with a plastic knife.

3. Now coat the yogurt pot with the plaster and push small pebbles round the base of the pot to look like rocks. Leave it to dry.

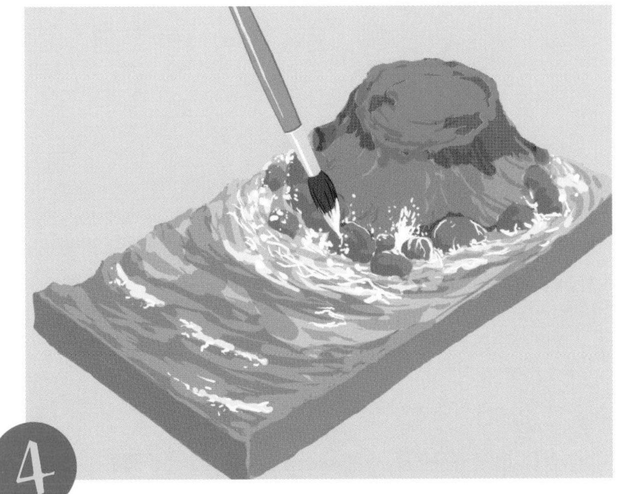

4

Remove the model from the box lid. Paint the island green and brown and the sea blue with white flecks, blending the colours for a realistic effect.

5

Now for the lighthouse. Roll a tapering tube about 10cm long from the clay, and add a strip round the top of the tower. When the clay is dry, paint it red and white, with a few black windows and a door.

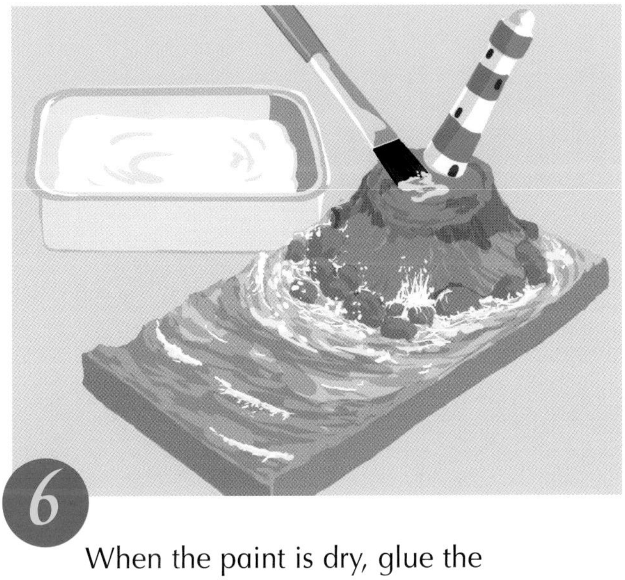

6

When the paint is dry, glue the lighthouse onto the island.

Salt-dough basket

If you don't have any clay, you can create your own! Salt dough is cheap and easy to make and can be used for all kinds of modelling projects.

1

Sprinkle flour on the salt dough and roll it out to about 2cm thick. Use a plastic knife to cut 15 strips.

You Will Need

- Salt dough mixture (see p7)
- Flour
- Rolling pin and plastic knife
- Kitchen foil
- Shallow ovenproof dish
- Old ball-point pen
- Paints: blue, red, green and brush
- Small scrap of green felt
- Scissors

2

Cover the inside of a dish with kitchen foil. Lay a line of strips across the bowl. Now weave a strip down the middle of the bowl in the opposite direction.

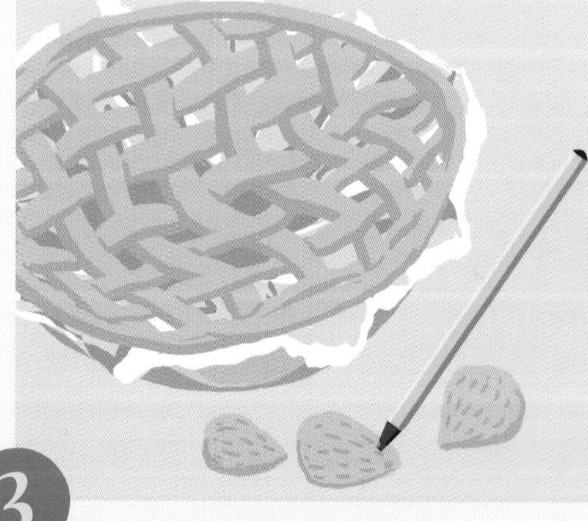

3

Carry on weaving strips to make a basket. Press a thin strip of dough all round the rim. Make strawberries from leftover dough, then poke holes in them with an old pen.

4

Bake the basket and fruit in the oven according to the instructions on p7. When they are cold, separate the dish from the basket. Paint the basket blue and the strawberries red with green dots.

5

Cut stalk shapes from the green felt and glue them to the tops of the strawberries. Then glue the strawberries to the edge of the basket.

Sheriff's badge

Make some salt dough, model yourself a lawman's badge and run those baddies out of town!

You Will Need

- Salt dough (see recipe on p.7 – use ¼ the amount)
- 6-cornered star cookie cutter
- Oiled baking tray
- Brooch backs
- All-purpose glue
- Silver paint and brush

1

Roll out the dough to about 5mm. Cut out some 6-cornered star shapes with the cookie cutter and put them onto an oiled baking tray.

2

Roll six tiny balls, wet the corners of the stars and stick a ball on each corner. Bake according to the recipe on p7. Then paint the star silver. Leave to dry, then glue a brooch back to the star.

TOYS and GAMES

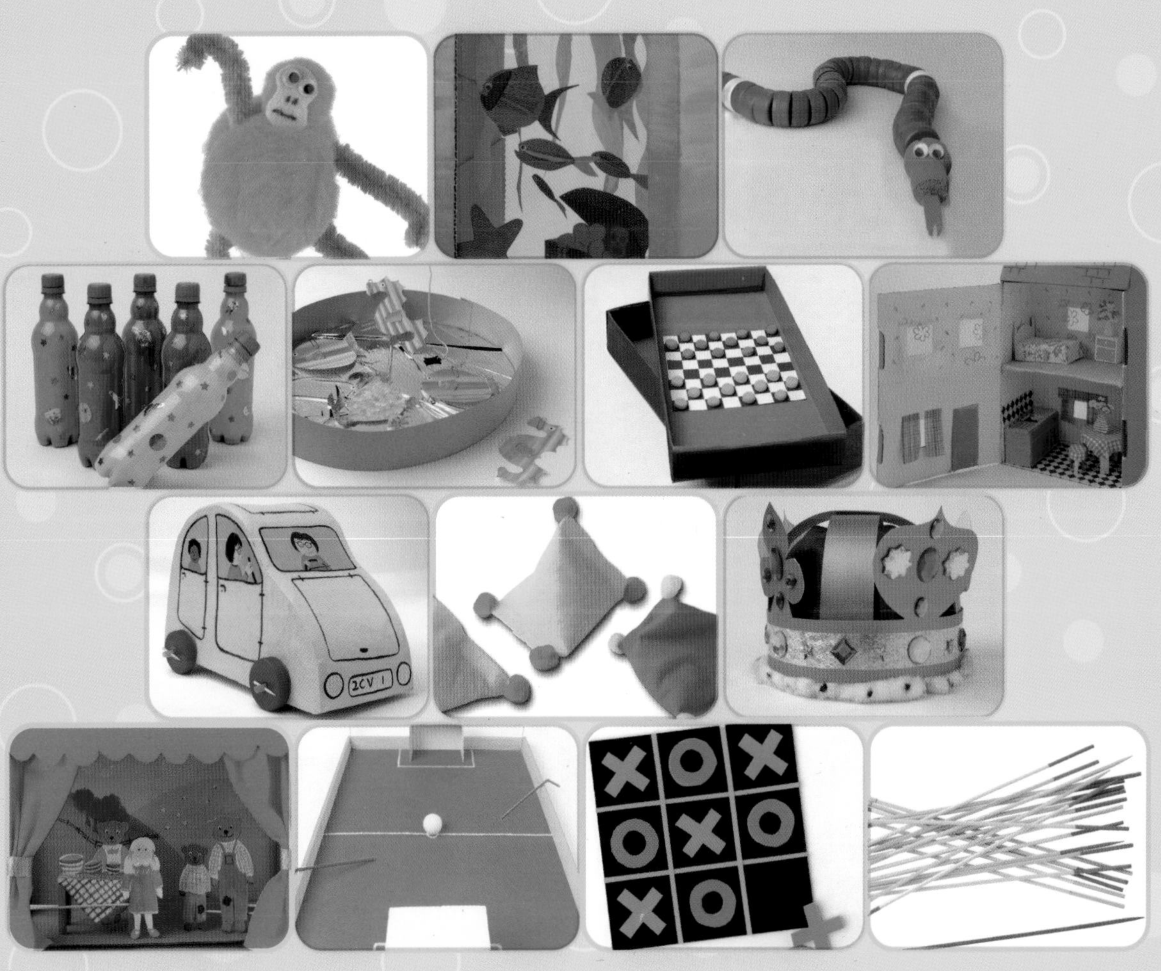

Funky monkeys

This pair of acrobatic monkeys love hanging around with each other! They are made from bendy pipe cleaners and fluffy pompoms.

You Will Need

- 3 x 30cm brown chenille pipe cleaners
- PVA glue
- 4 x 5cm pompoms
- 2 x 2.5cm pompoms
- Scrap of beige felt
- Black fine marker pen
- 4 tiny googly eyes

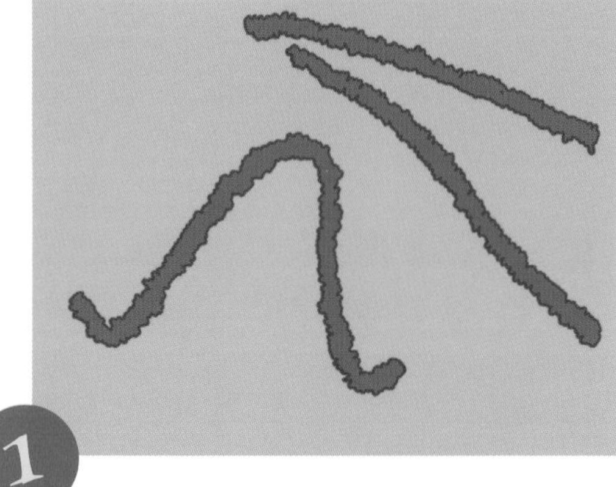

1

Cut the pipe cleaners in half to make 6 equal lengths. Bend one length in half to make the legs, then bend the ends to make feet. Repeat with another length for the arms and hands.

2

To make the tail, fix another pipe cleaner to the centre of the legs and arms, winding the end around at the bends to join them all together.

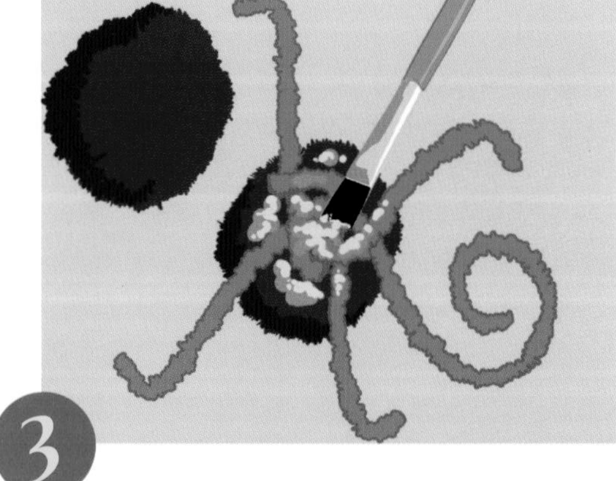

3

Use PVA glue to stick two of the larger pompoms together, sandwiching the legs, arms and tail between them.

4

To make a head, cut a small figure-of-eight shape from the felt. Glue googly eyes on the felt face and use the marker to draw nostrils and a mouth. Glue the face to a 2.5cm pompom.

5

Glue the head to the top of the pompom body and leave it to dry. Bend the arms, legs and tail into shape. Repeat for the second monkey.

Try This!

Creepy crawly

This terrifying tarantula is made from four pipe cleaners for the legs, with two pompoms holding them in place. Add eyes, antennae and a hungry mouth and he'll give your friends the shivers!

Shoe-box aquarium

Make your own sea-bed scene, complete with a chest full of sunken treasures. The best thing about these fish is they don't need feeding!

You Will Need

- Empty shoe box
- Set of paints
- Scissors
- Blue acetate film
- Sticky tape
- White paper and pencil
- Clear thread
- Tissue paper: light and dark

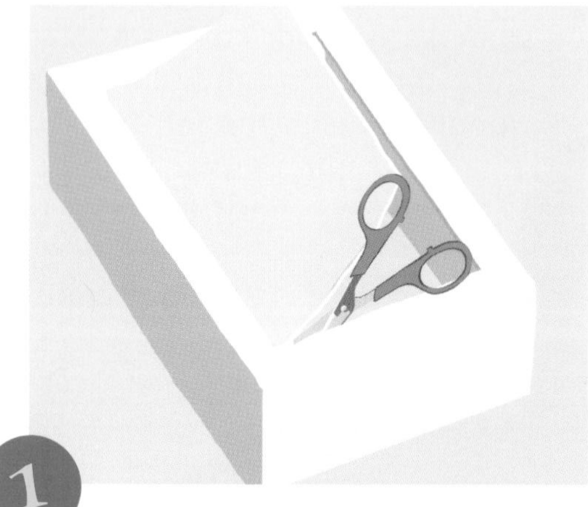

1 Cut the bottom out of the box, leaving a 2cm border all round.

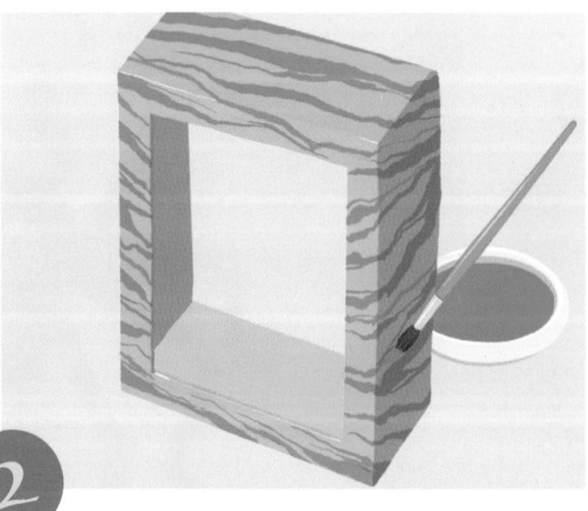

2 Paint the box light blue all over except for the floor. When it is dry, paint a few light green and darker blue streaks over it. Paint the floor sandy yellow.

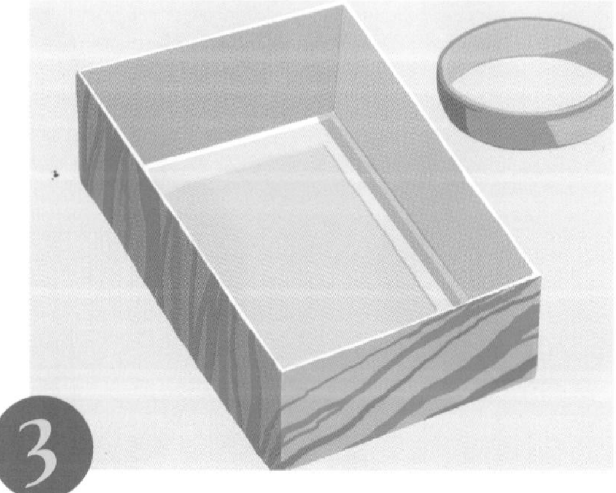

3 Cut a piece of blue acetate film to fit inside the window. Stick it in place with tape.

4

On white paper, draw and colour in different fish, a starfish and a treasure chest on a mound of brown sand. Cut them out.

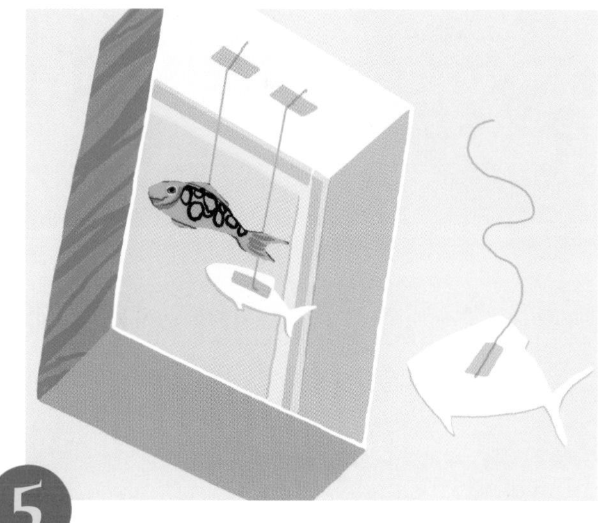

5

Use sticky tape to attach clear thread to the fish and tape the other ends to the box top, so the fish look as if they are swimming.

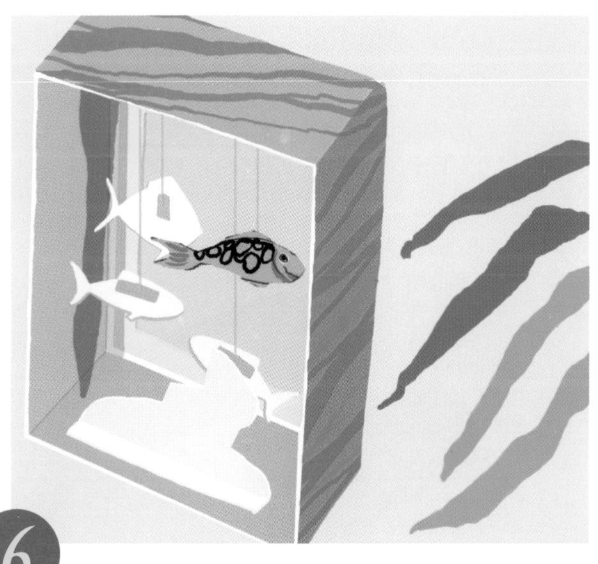

6

Cut four strips from the tissue paper and tape them to the top of the box so they hang down like seaweed. Tape the starfish to the side of the box. Fold down the bottom of the treasure chest and tape the flap to the floor.

Bottle-top snake

Use the tops of fizzy water bottles to make a super, slithery snake. Ask an adult to save you the two wine corks you need.

You Will Need

- Champagne-style cork
- Wine cork
- Green acrylic paint and brush
- Plastic bottle tops: 30 green, a few red and white
- Old ball-point pen
- 3 small screw eyes
- 60cm string
- Small bell
- 2 googly eyes
- Scrap of red felt
- Scissors
- PVA glue

1 Paint the two corks all over with the green acrylic paint. Leave to dry.

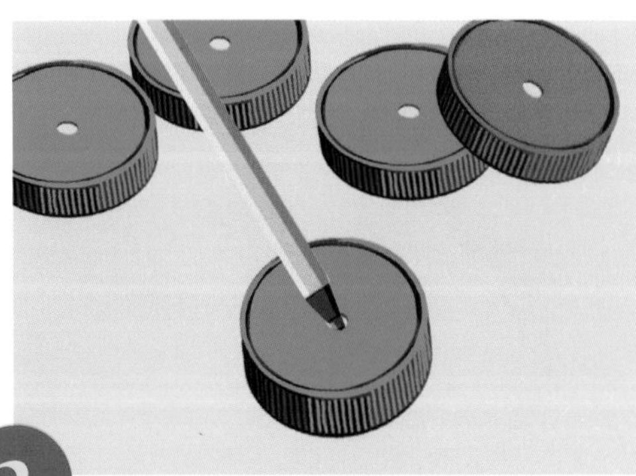

2 Using the old ballpoint pen, make a hole in the middle of each of the bottle tops.

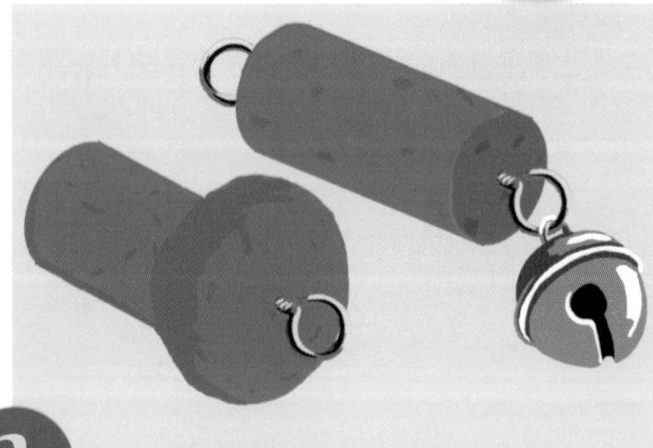

3 Screw one eye into the top of the champagne cork. Add the bell to another screw eye, and screw this and the remaining eye into each end of the wine cork.

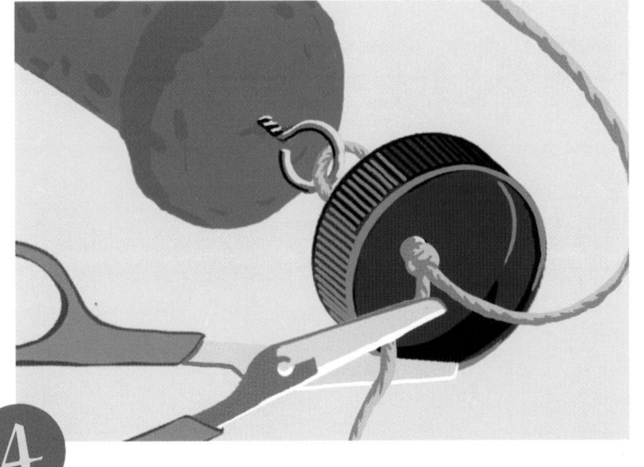

4

Thread one end of the string through the bottom of a green bottle top. Now thread it though the champagne cork eye and back through the bottle top. Make a knot and trim one end only.

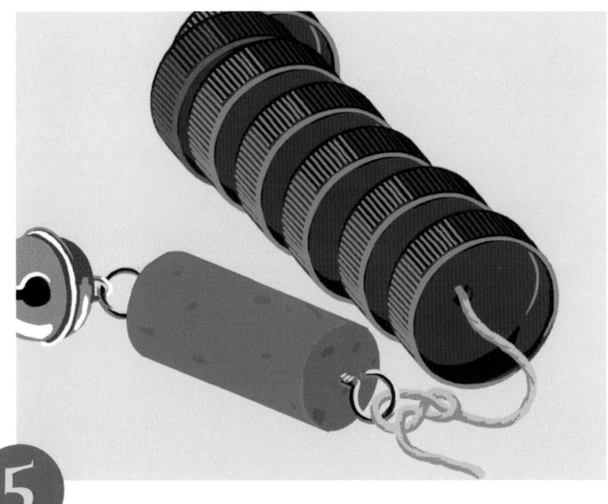

5

Thread all the bottle tops onto the string, keeping them all the same way round. Finish by tying the string to the screw eye on the wine cork.

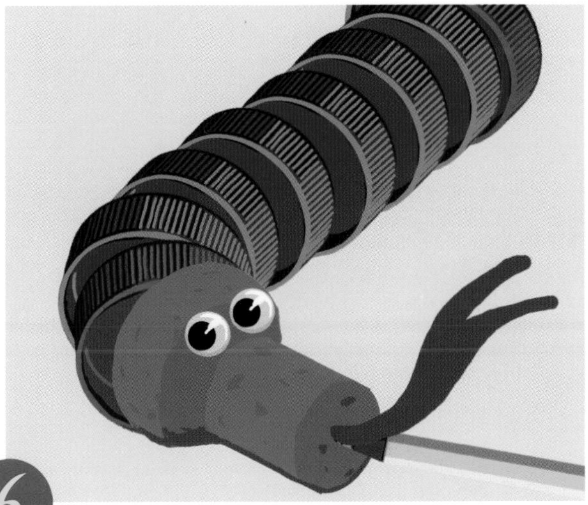

6

◂ Glue the two googly eyes in place. Cut a thin forked tongue from the red felt and use the pen to poke it into the cork.

Bottle skittles

Play skittles in the garden or, if it's raining, indoors – just don't do it anywhere near your mum's best china!

You Will Need

- 6 identical clear plastic drinks bottles with lids
- Ready-mixed paints: red, yellow, green
- Washing-up liquid
- Old jug
- Self-adhesive star and planet stickers
- Funnel
- Sand

1. In an old jug, mix the green paint with water until it looks like thin custard. Add a small squirt of washing-up liquid.

2. Pour some paint mixture into a bottle and put the top on. Shake the bottle to spread the paint all over the inside of the bottle. Add more paint if you need to, until the whole inside is covered.

3. Remove the top, pour out any remaining paint and leave the bottle to dry. Repeat for the other bottles, making three red, two green and one yellow bottle.

Put the funnel in the neck of a bottle and pour in sand to about halfway. This makes the skittles harder to knock over. Repeat for each of the bottles.

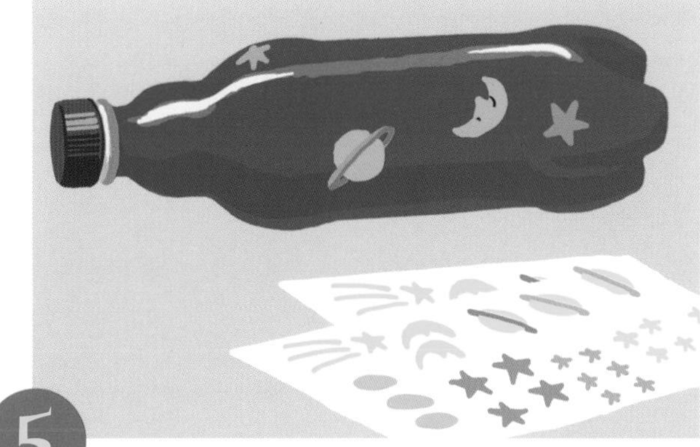

Put the tops back on the bottles. Decorate the skittles all over with star and planet stickers.

Top Tip

Painting the skittles from the inside of the bottle means that the paint won't chip when you play with them.

Fishing game

Challenge your friends to a game of magnetic fishing and see who can land the best catch!

You Will Need

- Sheets of white paper
- Pencil and scissors
- Set of paints and brush
- Foil paper
- Thick cardboard
- Sheet of blue card
- Sticky tape
- Paperclips
- 2 garden canes and string
- Magnets and hole punch
- PVA glue

1 Draw a fish, a crab and a seahorse. Cut them out and draw round them to make more. Make four fish, four crabs and two seahorses altogether.

2 Use bright-coloured paints to decorate the creatures and add eyes to the seahorses and fish. Glue coloured paper on the fish to make fins.

3 Cut 35cm ovals of card and foil and glue them together. Cut a strip of blue card about 110 x 4cm and put it round the card to make the rim of the pool. Tape the ends of the strip together.

How to play

Put all the creatures in the pool and take turns to fish them out. When all have been caught, add up the numbers on the bottoms – the winner is the person with the highest score!

4 Write the following numbers on the bottoms of the creatures : 2 on the fish, 5 on the crabs and 10 on the seahorses. Attach a paperclip to each creature.

5 Make two fishing rods by tying magnets to garden canes with string. Use thin, flexible magnets that are used for making fridge magnets. An ordinary hole punch will make a hole in these for the string.

Travel draughts

This miniature draughts game in a box is a great way to keep you and your friends amused on boring car or train journeys.

You Will Need

- Shoe box
- Paints: red, white, blue
- Paintbrush
- PVA glue
- Ruler and pencil
- Sheets of paper: 1 white, 1 blue
- Scissors
- Oven-bake clay: green and yellow

1 Cut round the bottom of the shoe box to make a tray about 5cm deep.

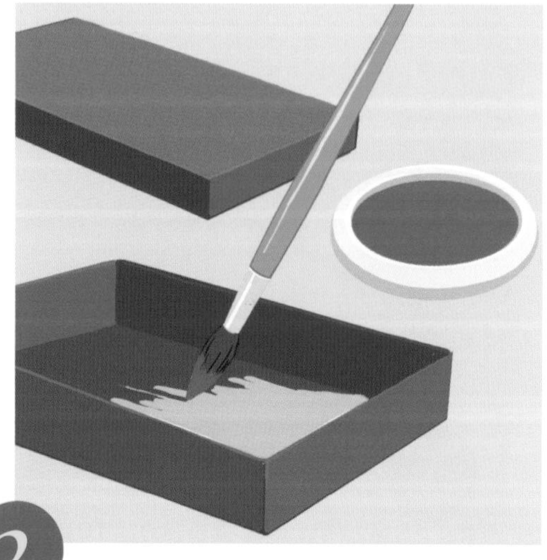

2 Paint the lid and the tray red all over. You might need to do two coats to cover all the lettering.

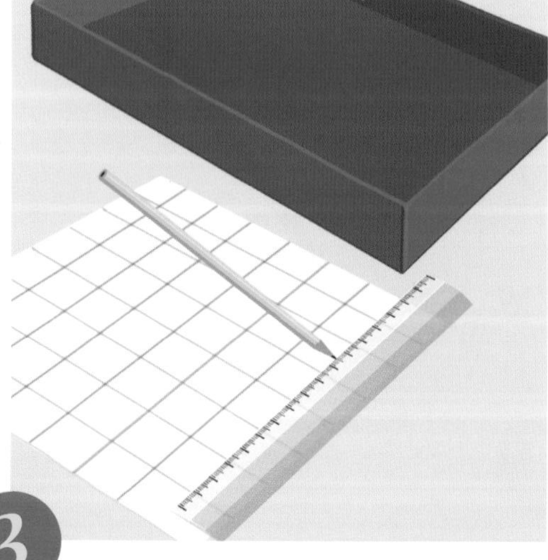

3 Measure the width of the tray and cut your paper into a square the same size. Draw a grid on the paper of 8 x 8 squares.

4

Make a grid exactly the same size on the blue paper. Cut out the blue squares and stick them onto the white grid, so that every other square is blue.

5

Spread PVA glue on the back of the paper and stick it down inside the box.

6

Roll each piece of clay into a sausage shape and use the plastic knife to slice each one into 12 discs. Bake them according to the maker's instructions.

Doll's house

Make your dolls a stylish new home. Although there are lots of steps, it's really simple to do. Turn the page to see the doll's house opened up.

You Will Need

- ✦ Trainers box with attached lid and sheets of thick card
- ✦ 3 x A4 sheets of thin white card
- ✦ Craft knife
- ✦ PVA glue
- ✦ Scissors
- ✦ Set of acrylic paints
- ✦ Coloured paper: black, cream
- ✦ Different scraps of fabric
- ✦ Sheet of tracing paper
- ✦ Small boxes and packets: eg. raisin boxes
- ✦ Kitchen foil

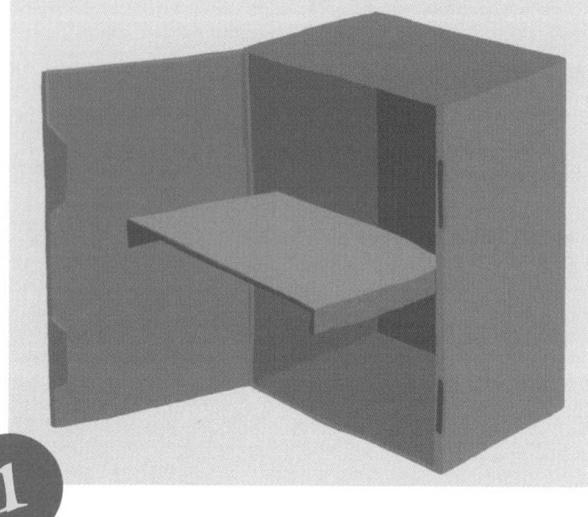

1 Cut a rectangle of thick card the same depth as the box and 4cm wider. Fold 2cm flaps on each side and glue them inside the box to make a floor.

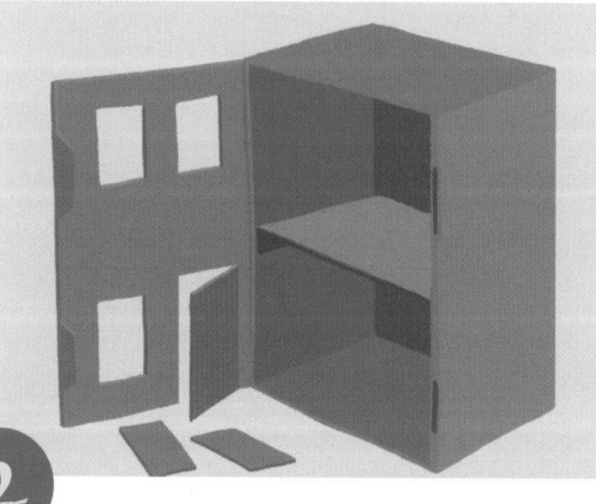

2 Draw three windows and a door on the box lid. Ask an adult to cut them out, using a craft knife. Only cut round three sides of the door shape, so it opens and closes.

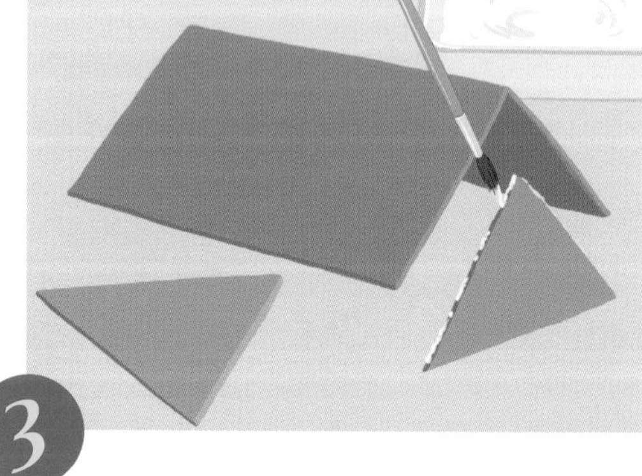

3 Cut a piece of thick card the same width as the box and twice the depth. Fold it in half. Cut out card triangles and glue them to each end to make the roof.

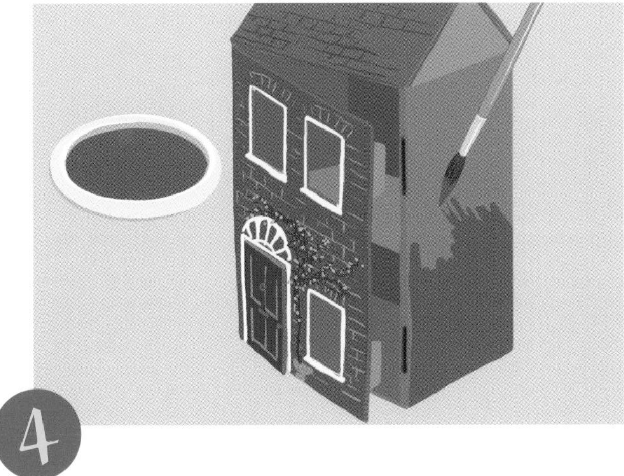

4

◂ Glue the roof to the house. Paint the outside of the house and the roof brown all over. When it is dry, use white to paint bricks on the walls. Paint round the windows and door. Add a climbing plant.

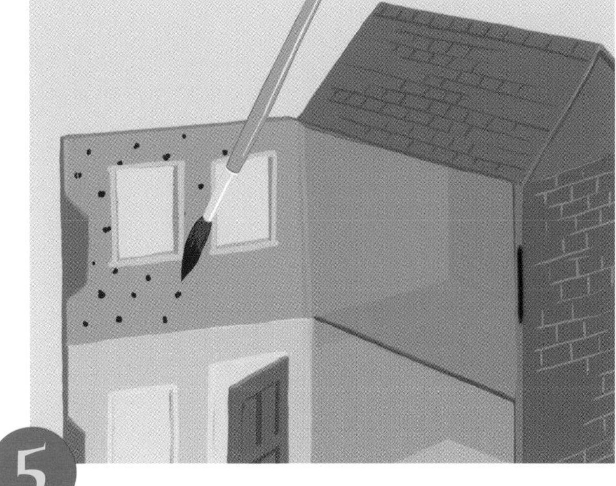

5

Decorate the bedroom. Use pink paint for the walls and add little spots with a dry brush to make wallpaper.

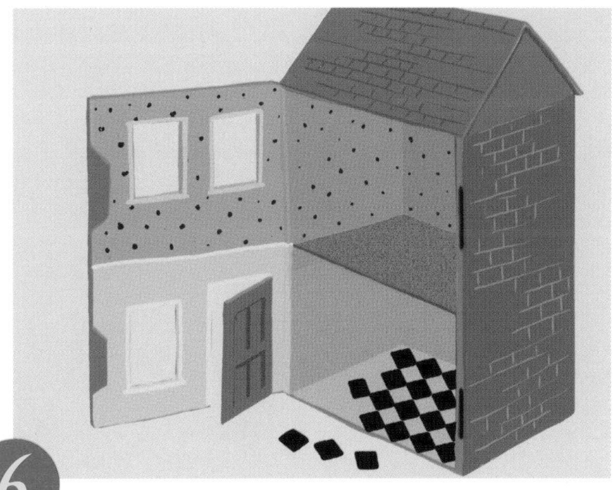

6

Glue a piece of fabric to the bedroom floor for a carpet. For the kitchen floor and splashback, glue little squares of black and cream paper to look like tiles.

7

◂ Cut small rectangles of fabric for the downstairs curtains and glue them to the tops of the windows. Draw patterns on tracing paper for blinds and tape them to the upstairs windows.

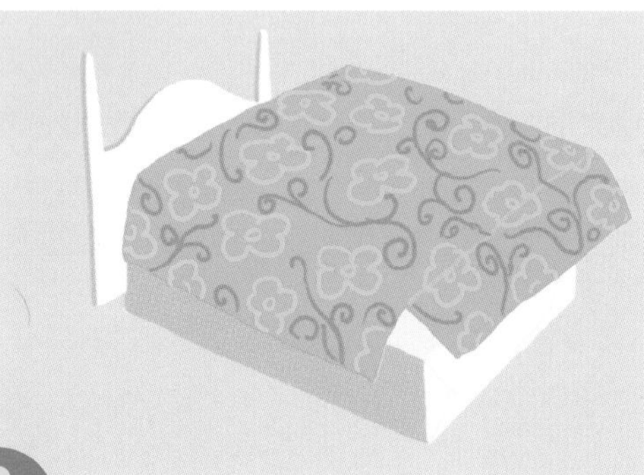

8 Cut a square of fabric and glue it to a small packet to make a bed. Cut a headboard out of thin white card and glue to the end of the bed.

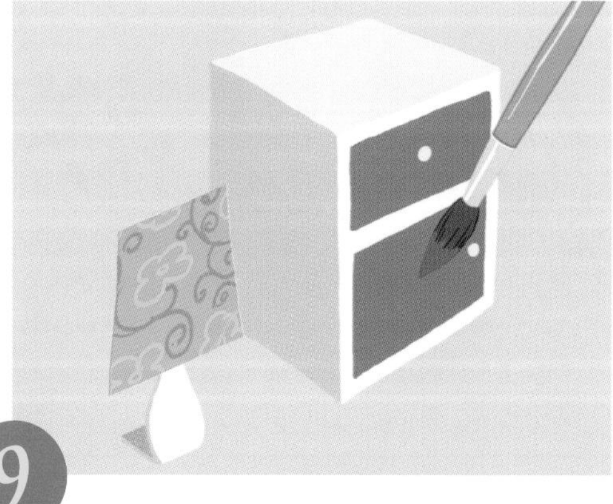

9

◂ Paint another small box brown and white to make a cabinet. Draw a lamp shape, with a small tab at the bottom, on the white card. Glue on a shade made from a scrap of fabric, then glue the tab to the cabinet.

10

For the table, draw round a small jar lid onto white card. Cut it out and glue on a strip of card all round it. Glue on three card legs, then glue on a square of fabric for a tablecloth. Draw a vase of flowers on the card, with a tab at the bottom. Cut it out and glue it to the table top.

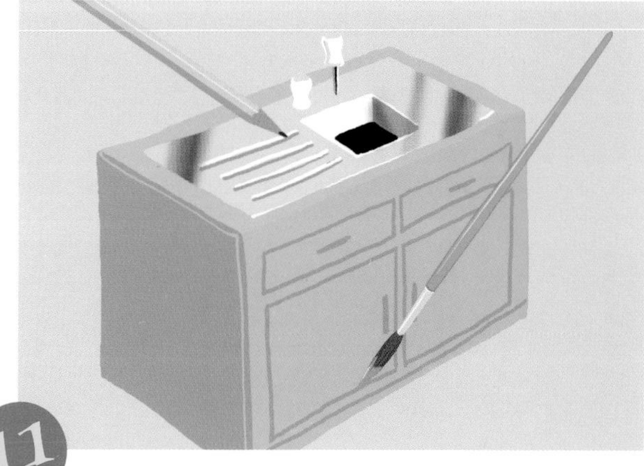

11

For the kitchen sink, paint a small box blue and draw on details for cupboards and drawers. Cut a hole for the sink in the top, and glue kitchen foil along the top, cutting a hole for the sink. Make grooves in the foil with a pencil. Stick two map pins in it for taps. Glue the sink to the kitchen wall.

Cardboard car

Vroom! This car has proper wheels, so it will whizz along a smooth surface. You can use the card from an old cereal packet to make the body of the car.

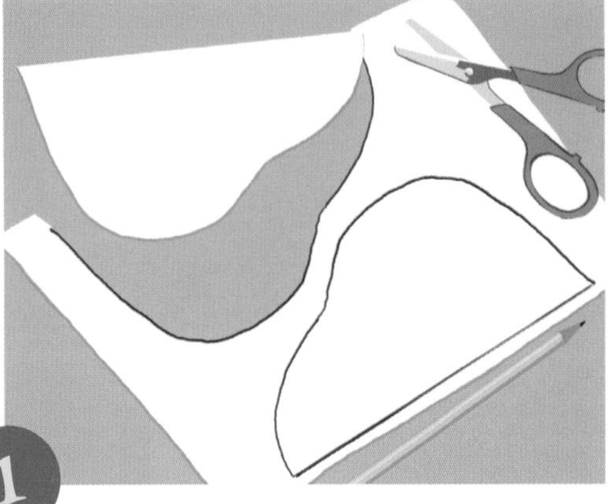

1

Use the template on p223 to trace two side views of the car. Cut them out. Cut out a rectangle 12cm wide and 42cm long.

You Will Need

- Sheet of card
- Scissors
- Masking tape
- Papier mâché paste (see p6)
- Old newspaper
- Sandpaper
- Set of paints and paintbrush
- 4 plastic bottle tops
- 2 straws
- 2 cocktail sticks

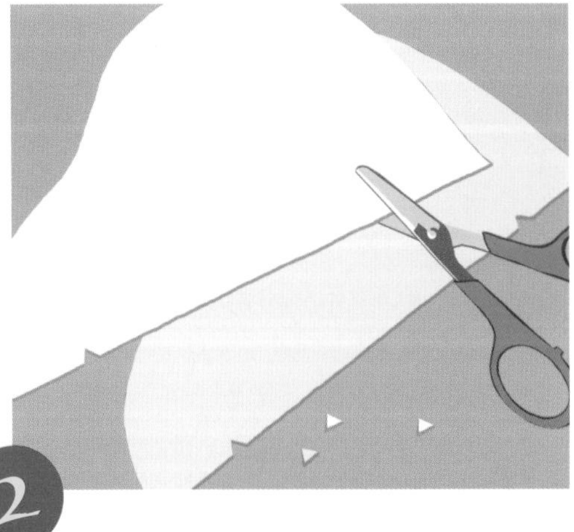

2

Snip out small V shapes 5cms in from the ends of each side on both pieces of the car.

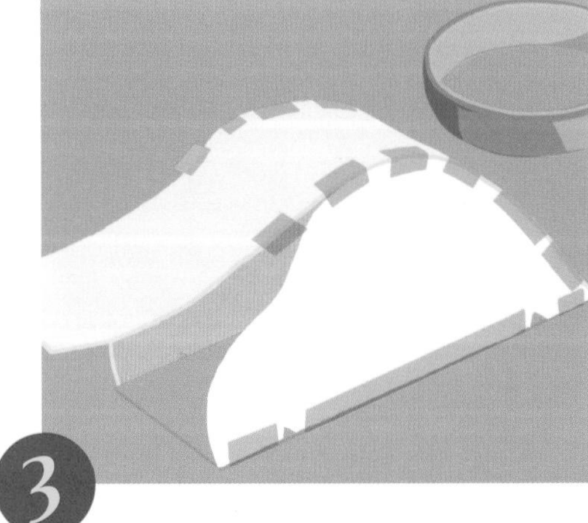

3

Tape all the pieces together. Cut a rectangle of cardboard to fit the base of the car and tape it on too.

4

Mix up some papier mâché paste (see p6) and tear up some newspaper. Cover the car in two layers of paper. Leave the model to dry.

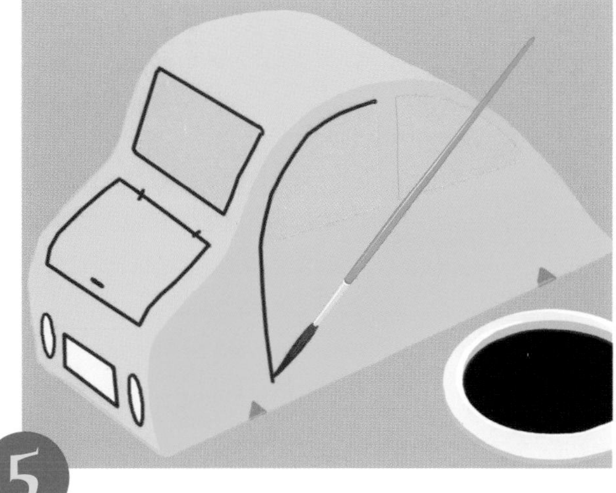

5

Rub the model all over with sandpaper. Paint your car yellow, then add windows, doors, a number plate, headlights, a driver and a passenger.

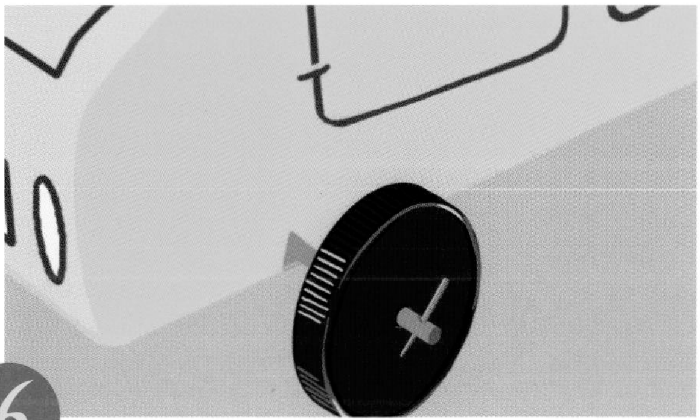

6

For wheels, make a hole in each bottle top. Push a straw through the hole and fix it with a small piece of cocktail stick. Push the straw through to the other side, trim it to fit, and add the other wheel. Repeat for the back wheels.

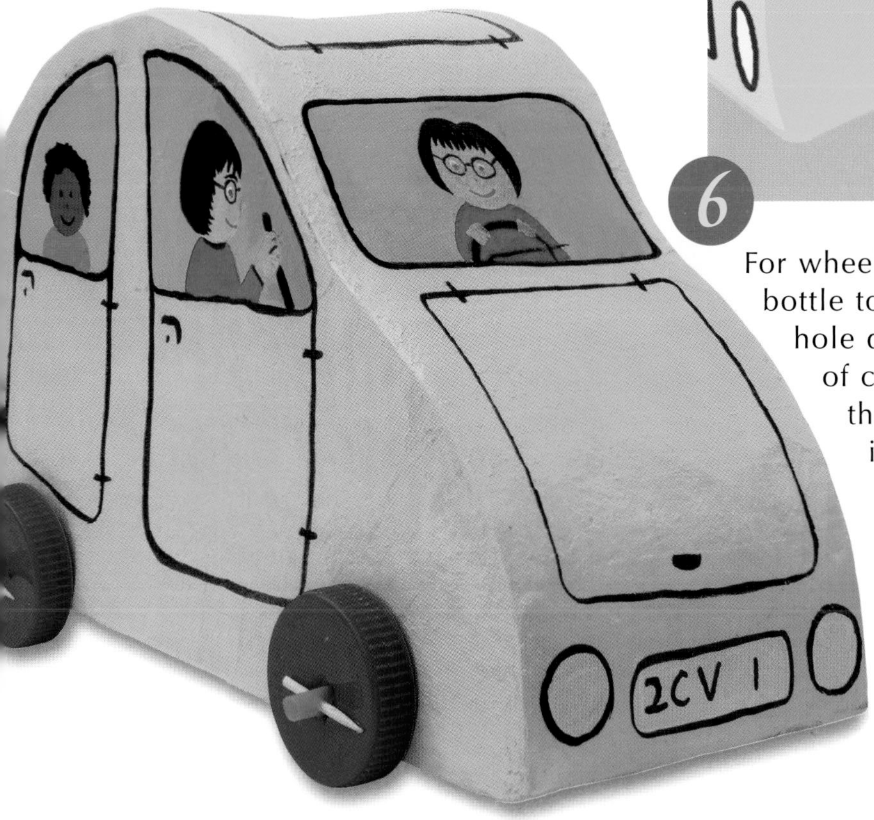

Juggling balls

These felt juggling balls are really quick and easy to make, leaving you plenty of time to practise your circus skills. You'll soon be a juggling genius!

You Will Need

- 3 felt rectangles 8 x 16cm: 2 yellow, 1 red
- PVA glue
- Scissors
- Small dried beans (eg mung beans) or lentils
- Spoon
- Pompoms: 4 yellow, 8 red
- Red and yellow thread and needle

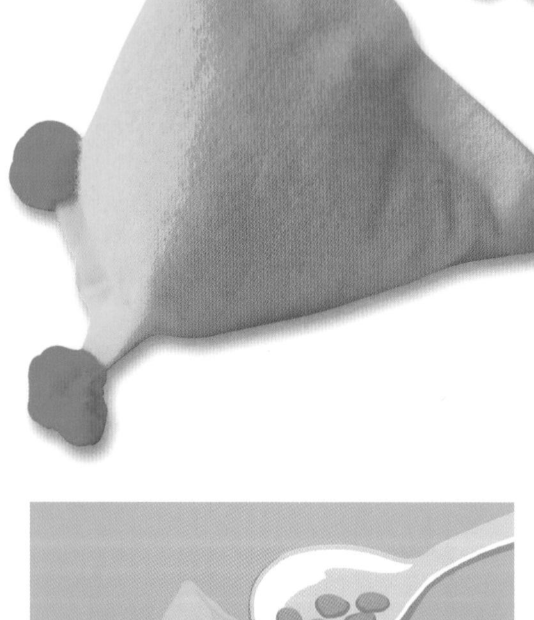

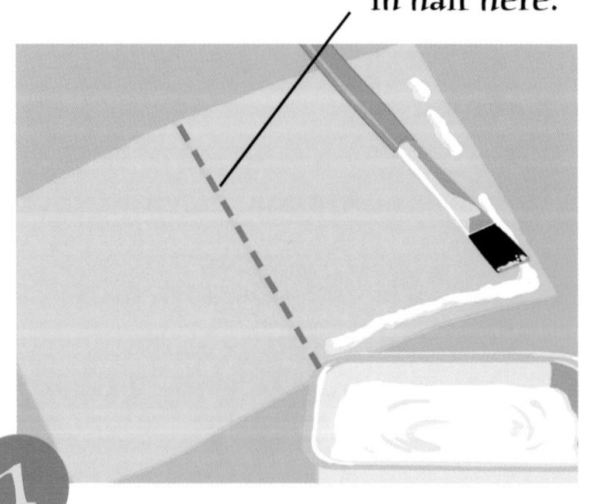

1 Take each felt rectangle and spread glue along one of the longer edges and along one of the shorter edges. Fold it in half and leave it until the glue dries.

2 Use a spoon to fill the felt bag about two-thirds full with the beans or lentils.

Try This!

Pyramid cushion

If you don't fancy juggling, make an Egyptian pyramid-shaped cushion instead. Start with a rectangle measuring 30 x 50cm and use hollow-fibre for the stuffing instead of beans.

Top Tip

If you want your juggling balls to be extra tough, sew round the seam of each ball after you have glued it.

3

Glue along the top of the bag and press the two sides together. Make sure the seam is in the middle of one side, to make a pyramid shape.

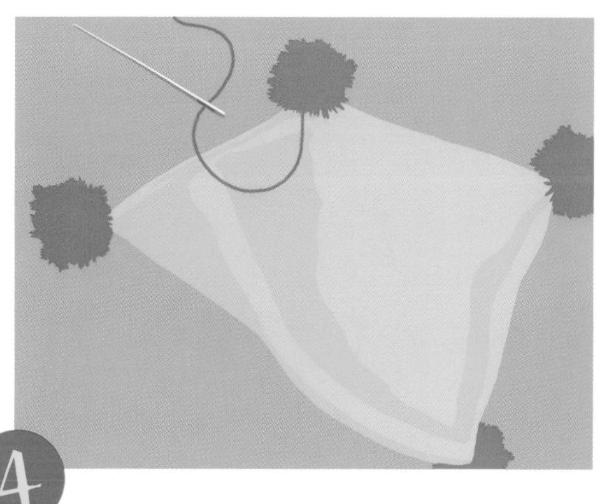

4

Using the needle and thread, sew a pompom onto each of the four corners of the juggling balls.

Royal crown

Make a jewelled crown. Then decide, will you be a merry monarch or a rotten ruler?

1

Trace the the crown template on p222. Transfer it onto the back of the gold card, then repeat, butting the second section up to the first. Cut out the whole strip.

You Will Need

- ✦ Strip of gold card, 12.5cm x 60cm
- ✦ A4 tracing paper and pencil
- ✦ Scissors
- ✦ PVA glue
- ✦ Hologram film, 25mm x 60cm
- ✦ 2 strips of gold card, 4cm x 33cm
- ✦ Paperclips and paper fastener
- ✦ Purple felt
- ✦ Large round plate
- ✦ Cotton wool
- ✦ Black paint and fine brush

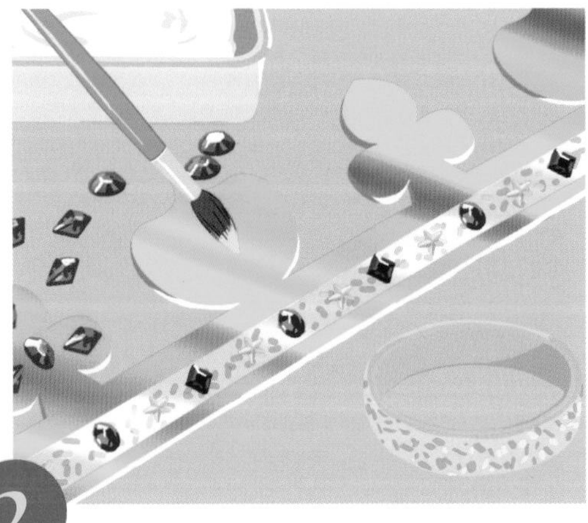

2

Glue the hologram film along the base, then glue gems along it and on the tops. Glue the two ends to fit loosely on your head, holding in place with paperclips.

Push a paper fastener through where the strips meet.

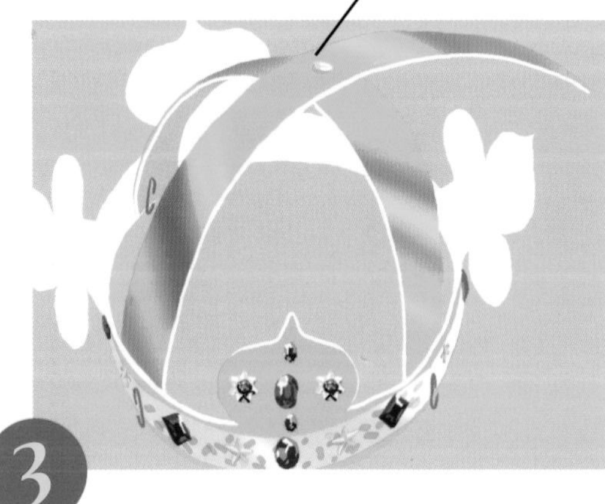

3

Make a mark halfway between the shapes. Glue the ends of the short gold strips over the marks. Hold them in place with paperclips while they dry.

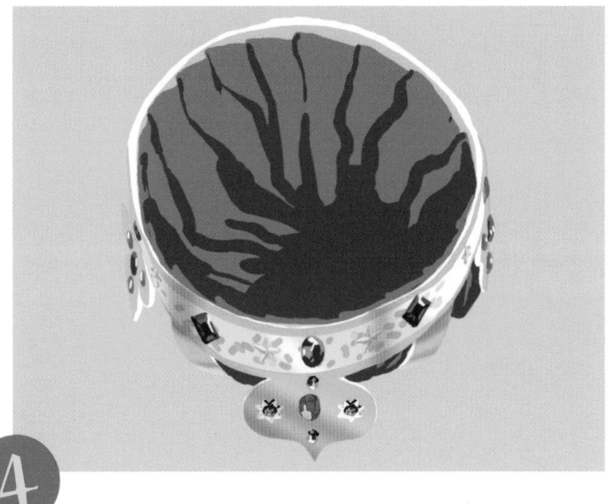

4

Trace round a dinner plate and cut out a circle of purple felt. Make small snips all round the outside of the circle. Put it inside the crown and glue to the inner brim, glueing bit by bit along the clipped edge.

5

Cut a strip of cotton wool about 4cm wide. Glue it all along the bottom edge of the crown. Paint black spots about 3cm apart along the length of the cotton wool.

Top tiara

Make a simple tiara, cut out with zig-zag scissors. Draw round a dinner plate onto the gold card, then cut the card in half and glue it to a simple headband. Decorate the tiara with shiny foil and stick-on jewels.

Miniature theatre

There's no need to be bored on a rainy day. Make a shoe-box theatre and get your friends to help you put on shows of your favourite stories.

You Will Need

- ✦ Shoe box, about 30 x 25 cm
- ✦ Scissors
- ✦ Pencil, paints and brush
- ✦ PVA glue
- ✦ 1 metre red fabric
- ✦ Gold ribbon
- ✦ Kebab sticks
- ✦ Sticky tape
- ✦ White paper
- ✦ Small square box eg. raisin carton

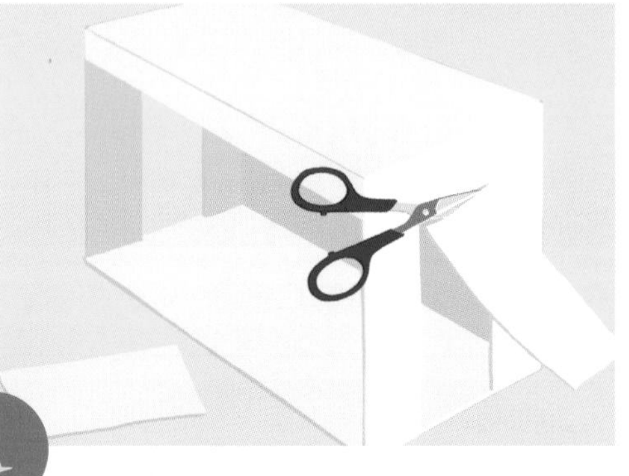

1 Turn the box lengthways and cut a window in each side.

2 Draw a country scene of hills, sheep and a blue sky with fluffy clouds on the back and sides. Colour the scene with paints.

3 Cut two pieces of red fabric 40 x 20cm. Glue them to the front of the box and decorate with gold ribbon. Cut a strip of fabric 80cm long and cut one edge into a scalloped shape. Glue it along the top.

4

Draw a picture of Goldilocks and the Three Bears onto thick white paper. Paint them and leave them to dry.

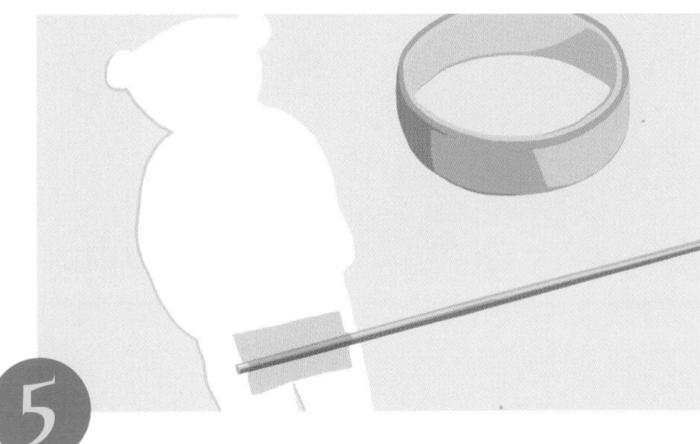

5

Cut out the characters and tape a kebab stick to the back of each, near their feet.

6

◀ Make a table by cutting into a small cardboard packet. Draw a blue checked tablecloth, cut it out and glue it to the table. Draw three porridge bowls and cut them out, leaving little tabs to stick them to the table.

Blow football

If you've got plenty of puff, try a lung-busting game of blow football. You can only move the ball by blowing through the straw – no handball allowed!

You Will Need

- ✦ Sheet of cardboard 70 x 50cm
- ✦ Green felt 90 x 70cm
- ✦ Sticky tape
- ✦ Wood glue
- ✦ Wood batons: 2 x 70cm, 2 x 50cm
- ✦ Acrylic paints: yellow, white
- ✦ Scissors
- ✦ Small cardboard box
- ✦ Red paper
- ✦ 4 cocktail sticks
- ✦ Drinking straws and ping-pong ball

1 Cover the cardboard with the green felt, pull it tight and tape it at the back.

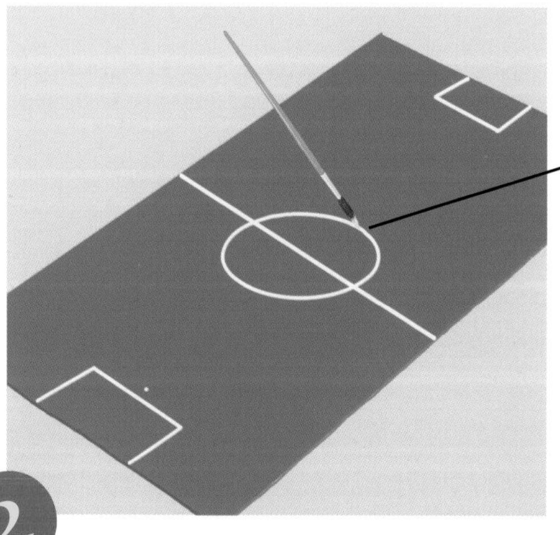

2 Turn it over and draw football pitch markings lightly in pencil. Paint over the lines in white.

You can use chalk for the lines, but you'll have to redraw the lines as it wears off quickly.

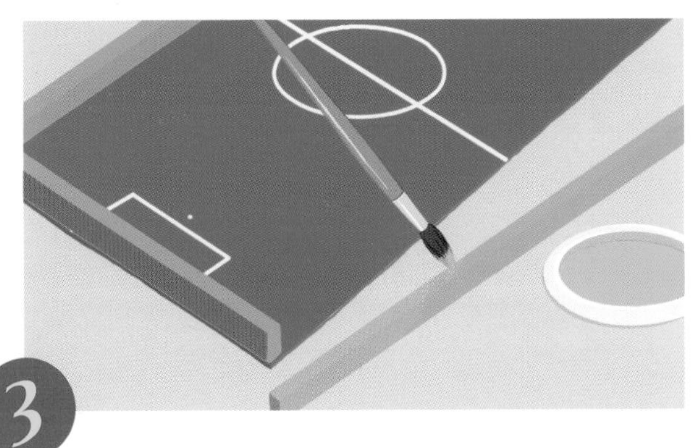

3

Paint the wood batons yellow and glue them together to make a fence around the pitch.

4

Cut a small cardbord box in half to make goals.

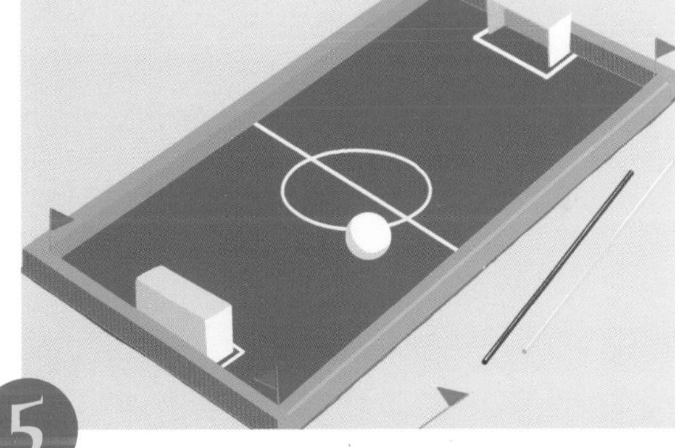

5

Put the goals inside the white boxes on the pitch. Cut out four small paper triangles and glue them to cocktail sticks to make corner flags.

Top Tip

Play a variation of the game with 10 coloured balls, 5 of each colour. The winner is the one who blows all their balls into the goal first.

Noughts and Crosses game

Be green and save paper by making a noughts and crosses game you can use over and over again!

You Will Need

- Funky foam: 1 sheet each in black, orange, purple and green
- Sheet of thick card 21cm square
- Ruler
- Scissors
- PVA glue and brush
- Paper and pencil

1 Cut a 21cm square of black funky foam and glue it to the sheet of thick card.

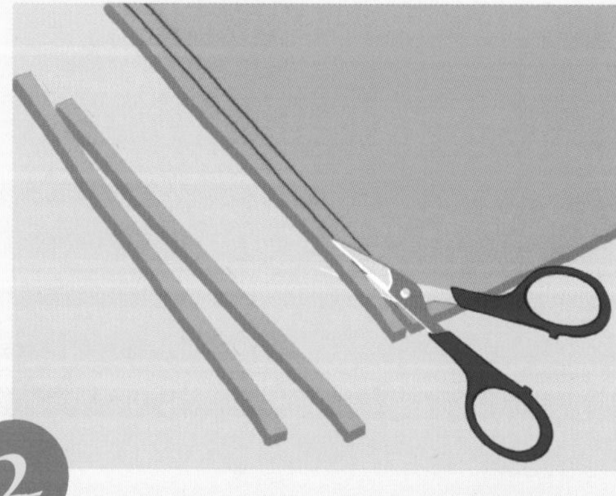

2 Use the ruler and pencil to draw four strips on the orange funky foam, 21cm long and about 7mm wide. Cut them out.

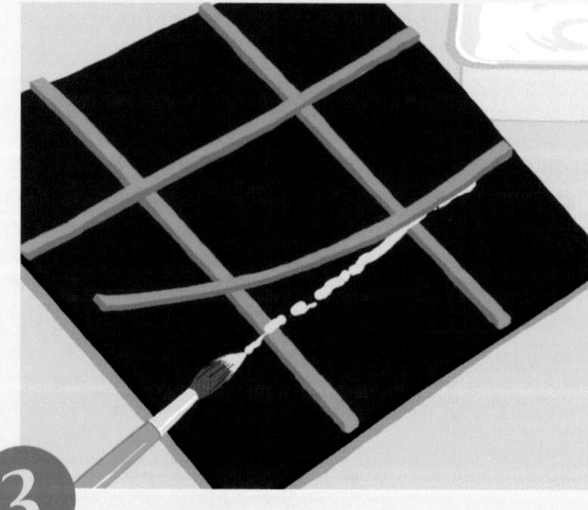

3 Glue the four strips of orange foam to the black foam in a criss-cross shape. You can use the ruler to help you position them evenly.

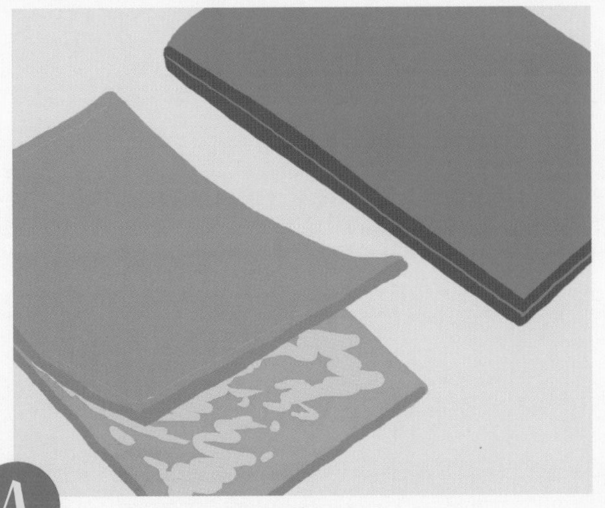

4

Cut the green funky foam in half and glue the halves together to make a double-thick sheet. Repeat with the purple foam.

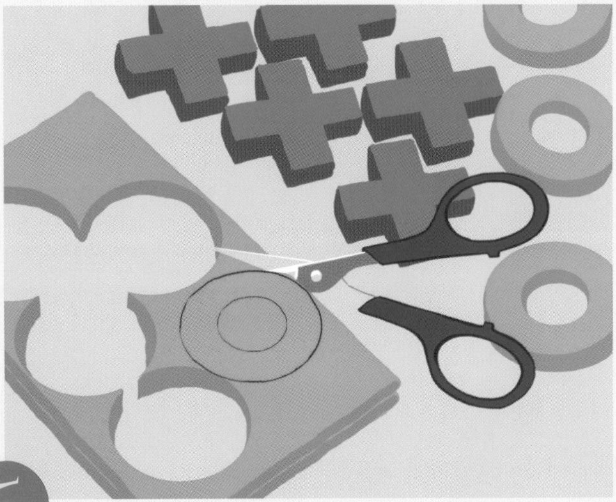

5

Draw a large cross and a nought onto paper. Cut the shapes out and trace them onto the foam. Make five green crosses and five purple noughts. Cut out the shapes, and you're ready to play!

Try This!

Easy peasy!

Instead of making your noughts and crosses, use shells and buttons to play with.

Pick-up sticks

To win this game you'll need a steady hand and nerves of steel. Be careful though – one false move and you'll be out!

You Will Need

- 25 kebab sticks
- Acrylic paints: red, orange, green, blue, purple
- Thin paintbrush
- Ruler and pencil

1

Line up six sticks in a row. Use a pencil and ruler to mark each stick 4cm from the end.

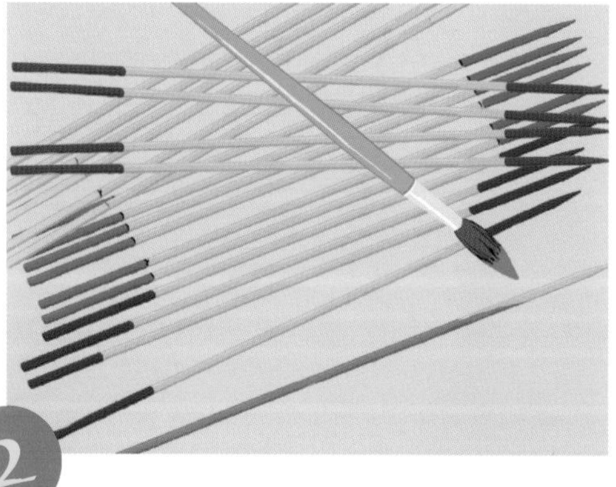

2

Paint the ends of the six sticks red up to the marks you made. Make orange, green and blue sets in the same way. Paint the last stick purple all over.

How to play

Drop all the sticks except the purple one in a random heap. Each player takes a turn to try to remove sticks from the pile, one by one, using the purple stick to help. You must only touch the stick you are aiming for – move any others and your turn is over! The player who removes the most sticks is the winner.

SPECIAL OCCASIONS

Easter chick card

Take time out from chomping on your chocolate eggs to make a pop-up card. Chicks are traditional symbols of Easter, and this one is super-cute!

You Will Need

- A4 sheet of white card
- A4 sheet of orange card
- Scissors
- PVA glue
- Pencil
- Felt-tipped pens or colouring pencils
- Sheet of yellow paper

1 Fold both sheets of card in half. Cut a 6cm slit in the white card in the centre of the folded sheet, at right angles to the fold.

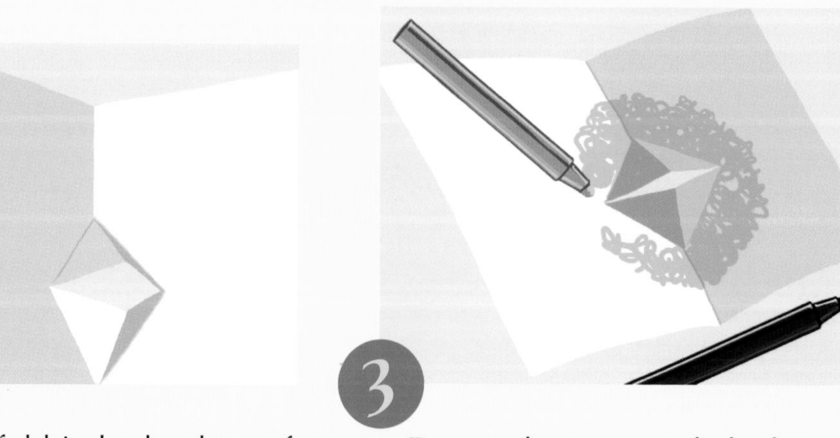

2 Carefully fold in both edges of the slit and make creases so that when you open and close the card, a beak shape pops out.

3 Draw a large, round chick's body around the beak shape. Use scribbly strokes to make your chick look fluffy.

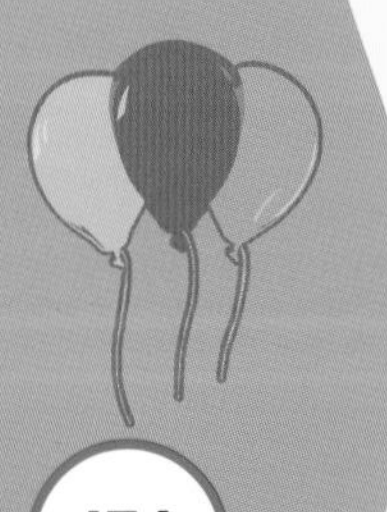

4 Draw black eyes and legs on the body. Cut two wing shapes from the yellow paper and glue them to the body. Make sure the wings stay inside the edges of the card.

5 Paste glue over the back of the white card, avoiding the beak part. Stick it to the orange card, and write 'Happy Easter' on the front of the card.

Try This!

Groovy chicks

Make a three-chick version by folding the card lengthways and cutting three slits for beaks.

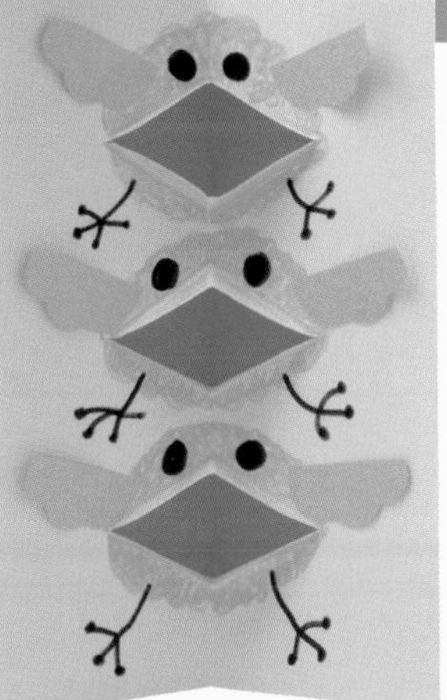

SPECIAL OCCASIONS

Chinese dragon

Dragons are symbols of good fortune in Chinese New Year celebrations. Maybe this colourful dragon will bring you luck – keep your fingers crossed!

You Will Need

- A4 coloured paper: red, yellow, green
- Scissors
- PVA glue
- Sticky tape
- Tissue paper: pink and white
- Pencil
- Paints: Black, red, yellow, gold, white
- Paintbrush
- Thick white paper
- Garden sticks

1. Cut the paper into 4cm-wide strips and glue them together until you have two strips, each about 120cm long.

2. Glue the two strips together at one end at right angles to each other. Put one strip over the other, folding it down. Repeat until the whole strip is folded.

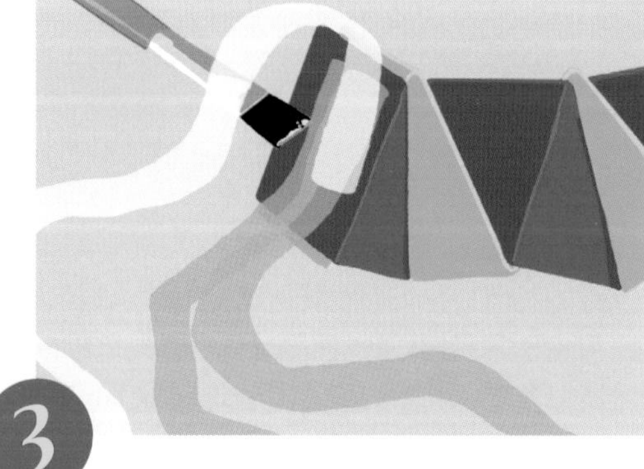

3. Cut strips of pink and white tissue paper and attach them to one end of the strip for a tail.

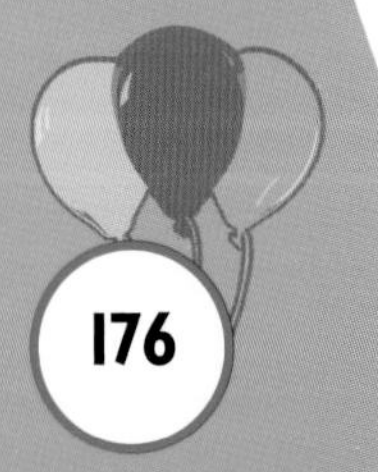

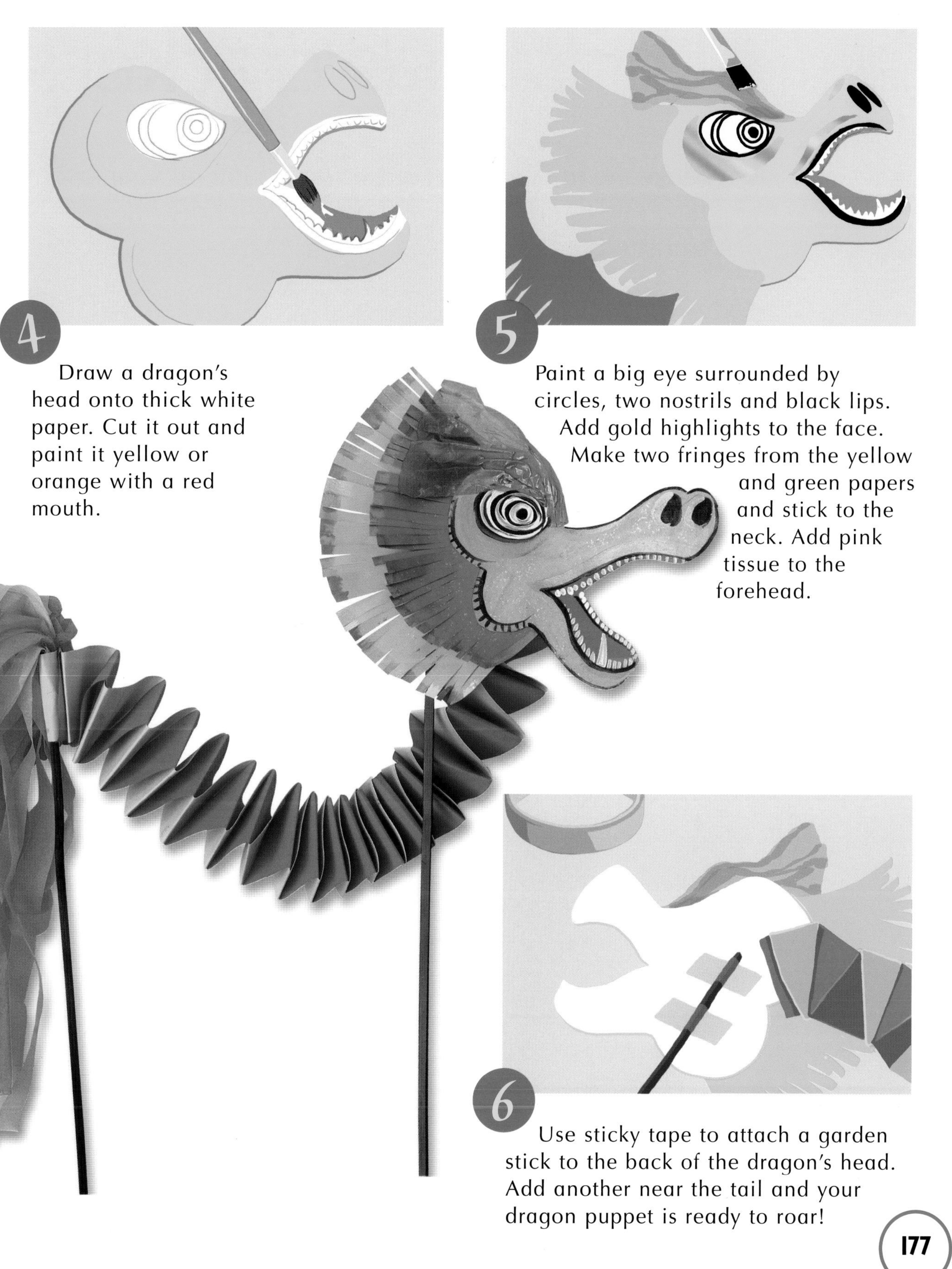

4

Draw a dragon's head onto thick white paper. Cut it out and paint it yellow or orange with a red mouth.

5

Paint a big eye surrounded by circles, two nostrils and black lips. Add gold highlights to the face. Make two fringes from the yellow and green papers and stick to the neck. Add pink tissue to the forehead.

6

Use sticky tape to attach a garden stick to the back of the dragon's head. Add another near the tail and your dragon puppet is ready to roar!

Christmas crackers

Make the family groan at Christmas. Put all your favourite terrible jokes in these home-made Christmas crackers.

You Will Need

- Crêpe paper
- Toilet roll tubes
- Zig-zag scissors
- Jokes on small pieces of paper
- Wrapped sweets
- Cracker snaps
- Rubber band
- Sparkly pipe cleaners
- Shiny hologram tape. and glue
- Small gift bows: red and green

1 Use zig-zag scissors to cut a piece of green crêpe paper three times as long as the toilet-roll tube and wide enough to go round it with a 3cm overlap.

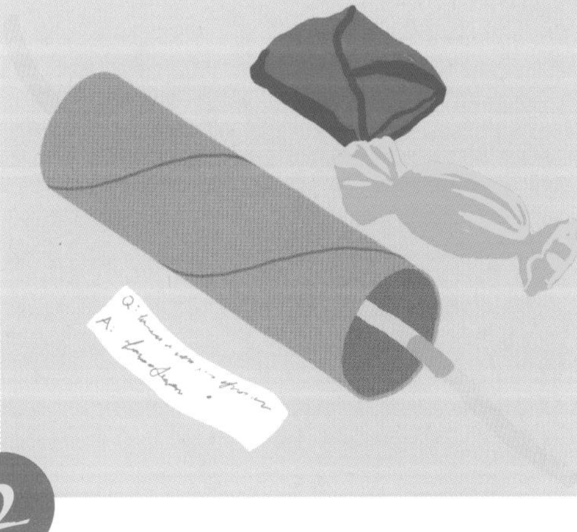

2 Put a wrapped sweet, folded paper crown, joke and cracker snap in the toilet-roll tube.

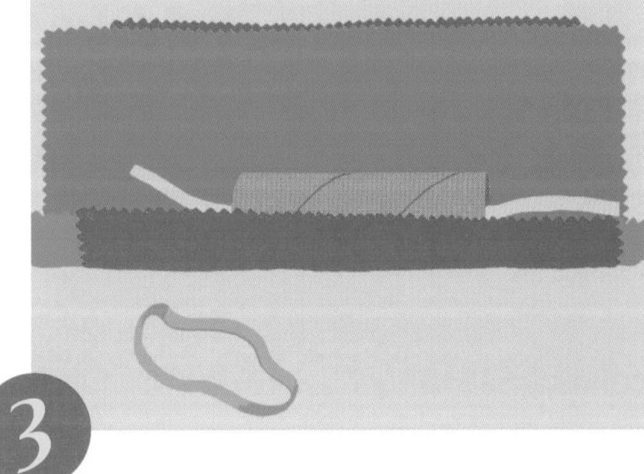

3 Cut red crêpe paper the same width but 2cm shorter than the green. Wrap both layers round the tube and hold them in place with a rubber band.

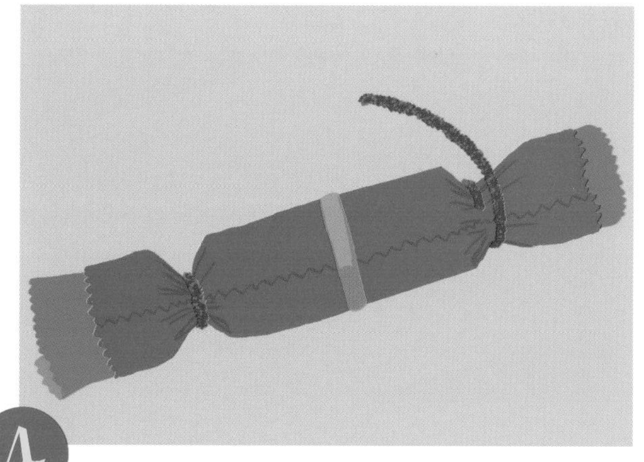

4

Cut 2 x 15cm lengths of pipe cleaners and wrap them round each end of the crackers.

5

Cut 2 strips of hologram tape and glue them round the tube. Remove the rubber band and decorate the tube with a gift bow.

Try This!

Paper crowns

It's easy to make paper crowns. Cut a piece of tissue paper about 15cm x 60cm. Glue both ends together and fold it in half twice, Cut the paper to a point. Open it out and you'll find a crown!

SPECIAL OCCASIONS

Halloween bat card

When you've finished trick-or-treating, make a spooky bat silhouette card for a really horrid halloween gift!

1

Fold the black card in half. Glue the orange paper to the front of the card, placing it centrally to leave a black border all round.

You Will Need

- A4 sheet of black card
- Sheet of orange paper 120 x 185mm
- Tracing paper and pencil
- A5 sheet black paper
- Scissors
- Stick of glue
- 2 round green sequins

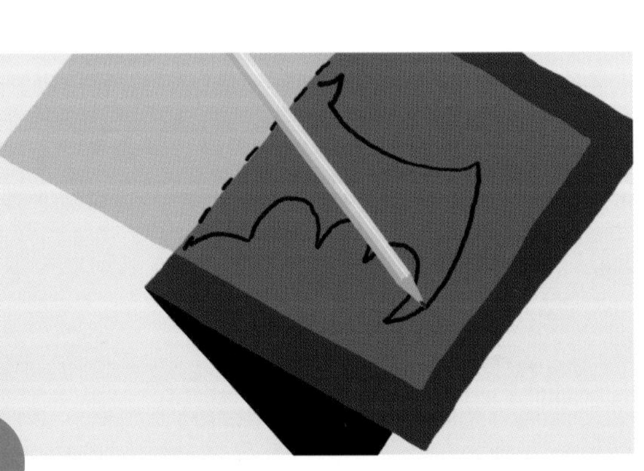

2

Trace the shape on p221 onto tracing paper. Fold a sheet of black paper in half and put the tracing paper on top. Trace down the half-bat shape.

Top Tip

Trace marks can be quite hard to see on the black paper. If you're good with scissors, cut out the bat instead - line up the tracing paper so the edge of the bat is at the edge of the black paper. Grip both pieces of paper tightly and cut round the bat shape.

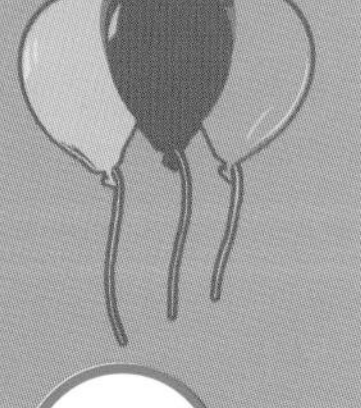

3

Cut out the half-bat, leaving the fold uncut. Open out the bat and apply glue over it. Stick it down at an angle on the front of the card.

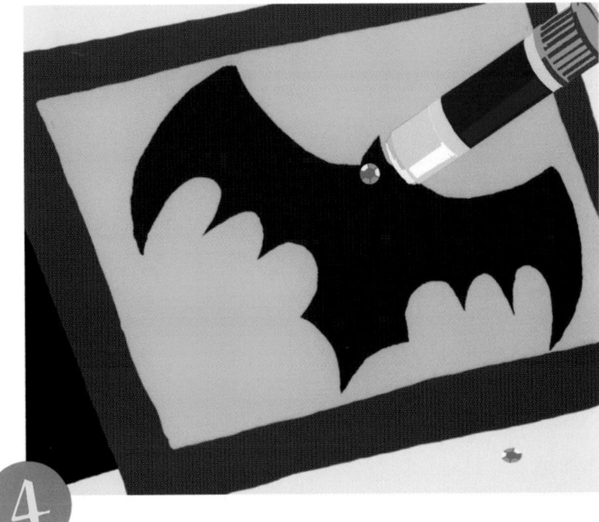

4

Stick on green sequins with a dab of glue to add menacing bat's eyes.

Easter choc nests

Cook an Easter treat for the family with yummy chocolate nests. Don't forget to get an adult to help.

1

Put the sugar, cocoa powder, butter and syrup in a saucepan.

You Will Need

For 5 nests:

- 75g sugar
- 75g butter
- 75g cocoa powder
- 2 tbsp golden syrup
- 75g shredded wheat
- Kitchen foil
- Medium saucepan
- Metal spoon
- Mini chocolate eggs

2

Place the pan on a low heat and stir slowly until the mixture melts. Don't let it boil!

3

Let the mixture cool slightly. Scrunch up the shredded wheat and mix it in.

4

Make the aluminium foil into five bowl shapes. Put some mixture in and press in the middle to make nests. Put them in the fridge to cool and set.

5

When the nests are hard, remove the foil and fill the chocolate nests with mini eggs.

Hanukkah candlestick

Jewish people celebrate the Hanukkah festival by lighting special candles and giving each other gifts. This special candlestick is called a menorah.

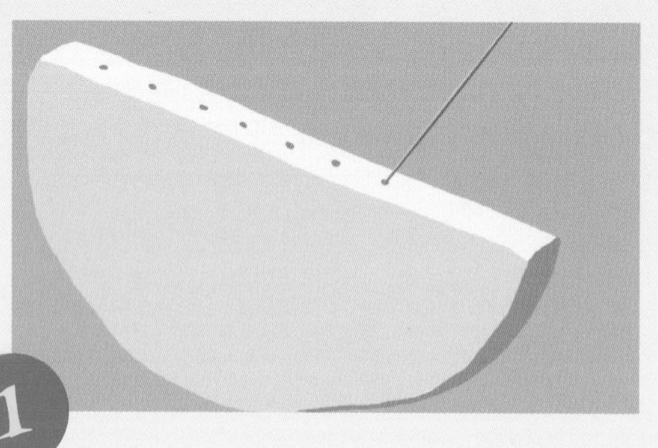

1

Roll out the clay to 2cm. Put the template (see p220) onto the clay and cut round it. On the flat end, using your cocktail stick, pierce nine small holes to mark the position of the candles.

You Will Need

- Tracing paper and pencil
- 500g air-hardening clay
- Rolling pin
- Plastic knife
- Cocktail stick
- Ruler and old pen
- Gold paint and paintbrush
- 9 small candles

Make a mark on the pencil so you know how far down to push.

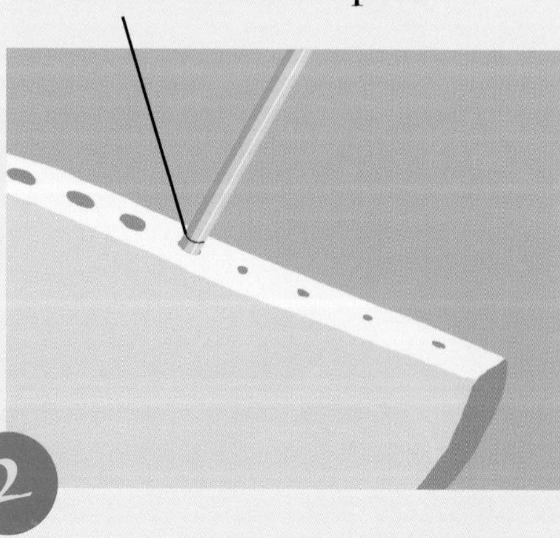

2

Push the end of the pencil about 1cm into the holes. Do this for all except the middle hole which should only be 5mm deep, so the candle will stand taller.

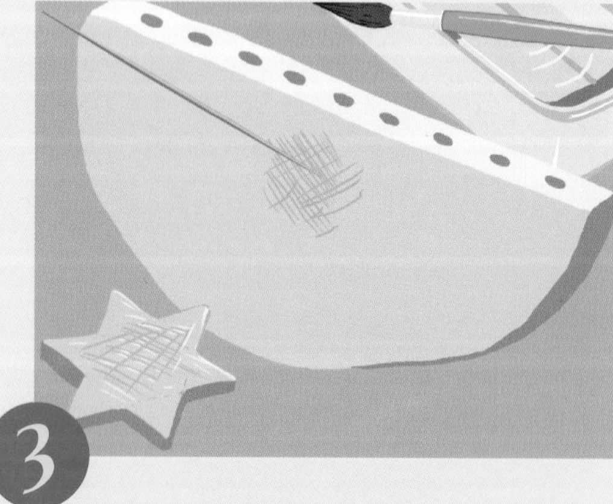

3

Roll out a small piece of clay and cut out a star using the template. Fix it to one side of the candlestick by wetting and scoring both pieces.

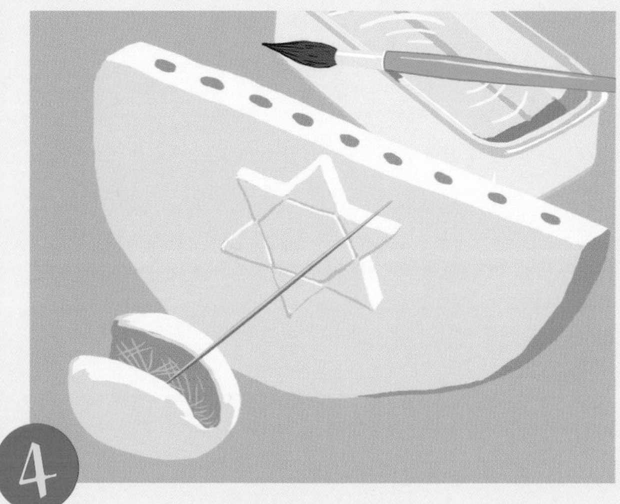

Roll a 5cm ball of clay. Flatten the bottom and make a groove along the top. Stick it to the bottom of the candlestick. Make sure it stands firmly and leave it to dry.

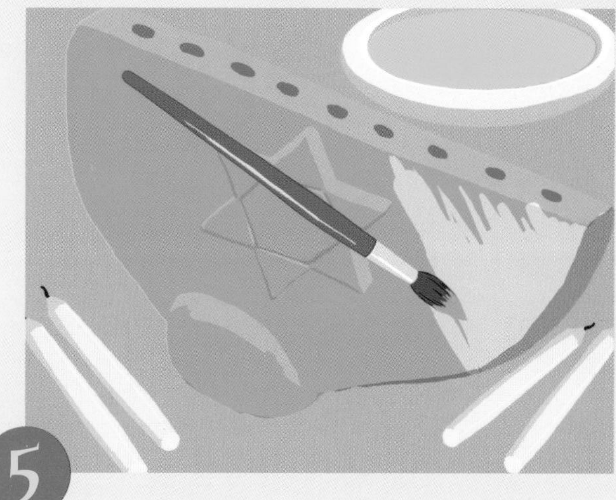

Paint the candlestick gold all over and leave it to dry. Insert the nine candles into the candlestick holes and ask an adult to light them.

Snowmen card

Make these great cut-out Christmas cards for all your friends. They're 'snow' cool!

You Will Need

- A4 sheet white card
- Pencil and ruler
- Scraps of black card
- Felt-tipped pens
- Silver glitter
- PVA glue and brush

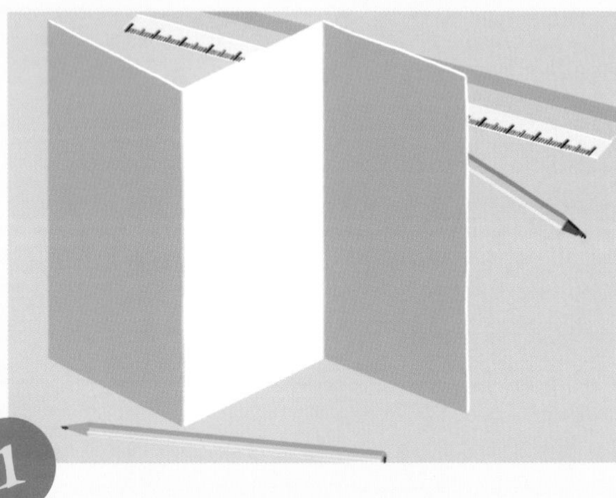

1

Mark the card along the long side, at 99mm and 198mm. Fold the card at these points to make three sections.

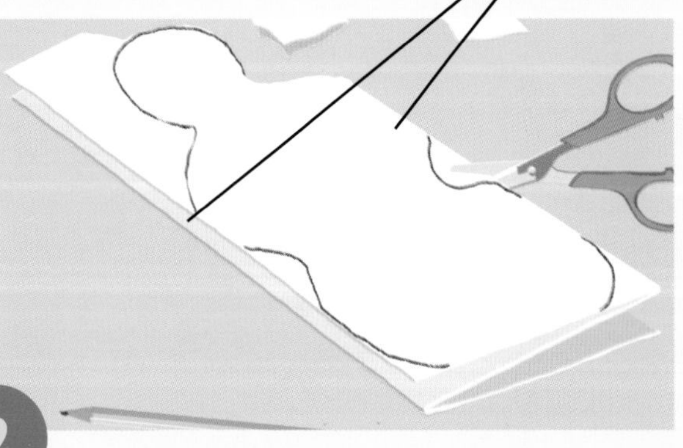

2

Draw a snowman shape on the card. Cut out the snowman, leaving it joined at the sides.

Try This!

Pudding card

Make a Christmas pudding card with brown-painted card. Draw round a small saucer, cut it out and stick on some paper holly and berries.

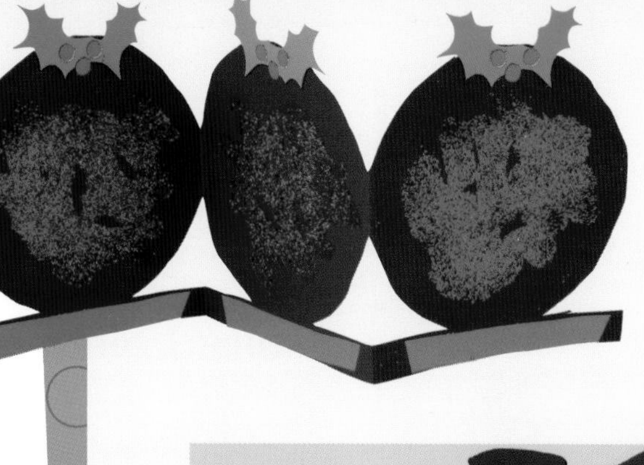

Dab on some glue and sprinkle on silver glitter for a sparkly finishing touch.

3

Open up the card. Cut three hats from the black card and stick them on the snowmen's heads.

4

Use the felt-tipped pens to draw eyes, mouths and buttons. Finish with orange carroty noses, walking sticks and scarfs.

Advent calendar

Start your countdown to Christmas with this Advent calendar. Fill the boxes with your favourite sweets and give yourself a daily treat while you wait!

You Will Need

- A2 sheet green card
- Sheet of thick card, 20cm taller than the green card
- A5 sheet red card
- PVA glue
- Gold card
- Soft pencil and rubber
- Scissors
- 23 small empty matchboxes plus one large one
- Silver and red foil wrapping paper
- Gold gift ribbon cut into 24 x 50cm lengths
- Large star sequins
- 25 wrapped sweets or chocolates
- Gold marker pen

1

Glue the green card upright to the thick card, leaving space at the top and bottom. Cut out a star from the gold card and glue it at the top. Trim the edges of the red card to make a pot shape and glue it at the bottom.

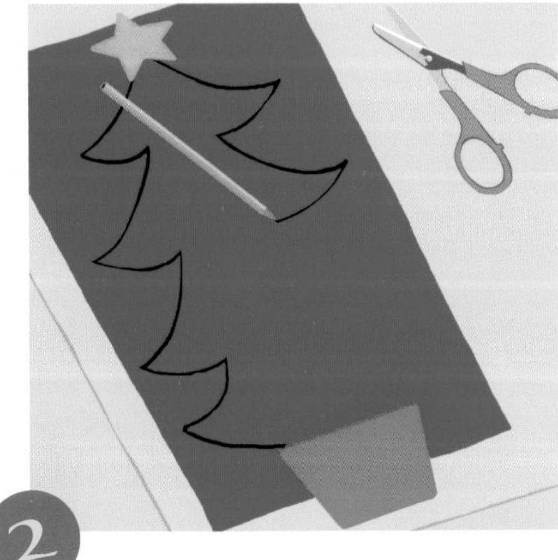

2

Draw a large Christmas tree shape on the green card and cut the whole shape out.

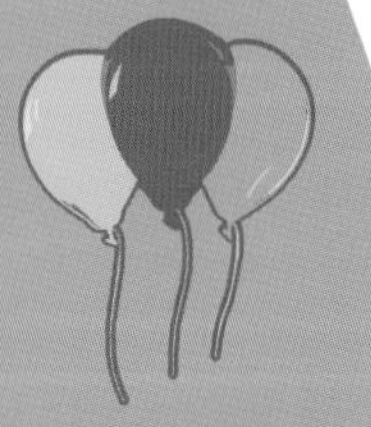

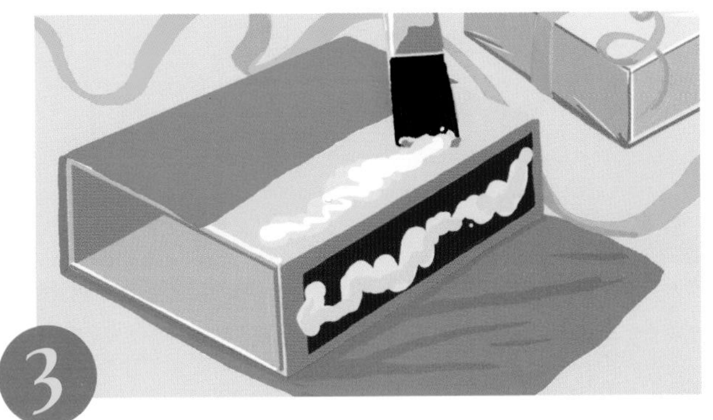

3

◂ Cover 12 matchboxes in red foil paper and 12 in silver. Tie a length of gift ribbon round each matchbox and tie a double knot in it. Curl the ribbon by running it between your thumbnail and index finger.

4

Using the gold marker pen, number each of the small boxes from 1 to 23. Write '24' on the big matchbox. Put a wrapped sweet in each box, and put two in the 24 box.

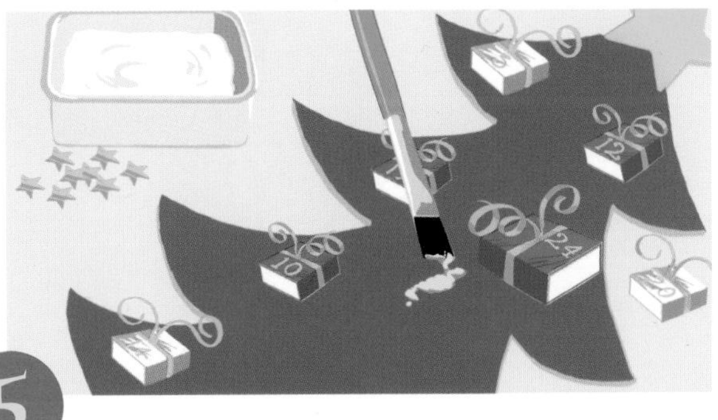

5

Arrange boxes 1-23 randomly on the Christmas tree and put the 24 box in the middle. Glue all the boxes in place. Glue sequin stars onto the tree in the gaps between the boxes.

Mother's day photo wallet

Mum will love to keep her favourite pictures of you in this cool photo album.

You Will Need

- 2 pieces of thick card 150 x 150mm
- 2 sheets A4 purple paper
- Sticky tape
- PVA glue
- 1 metre turquoise ribbon
- Sheet of turquoise paper 150x600mm
- Pencil and ruler
- Blue corrugated card 100 x 100mm
- Small square of purple felt
- Zig-zag scissors
- Gems to decorate

1 Wrap each sheet of purple paper round a square of card and fix in place with sticky tape.

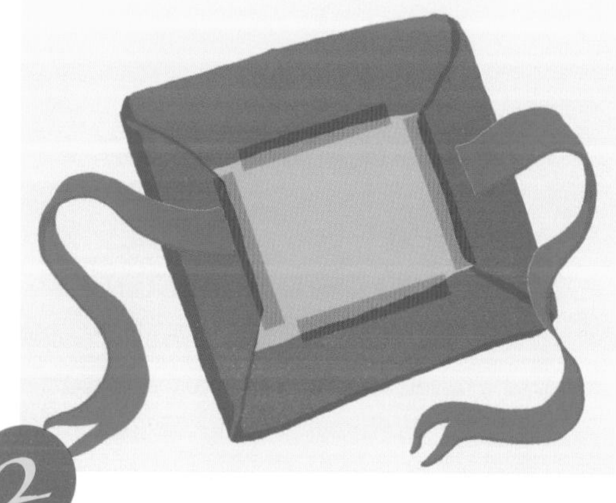

2 Cut the ribbon into four equal strips. Glue to the back of the purple cards, as shown above. Trim the end of each ribbon into a V shape.

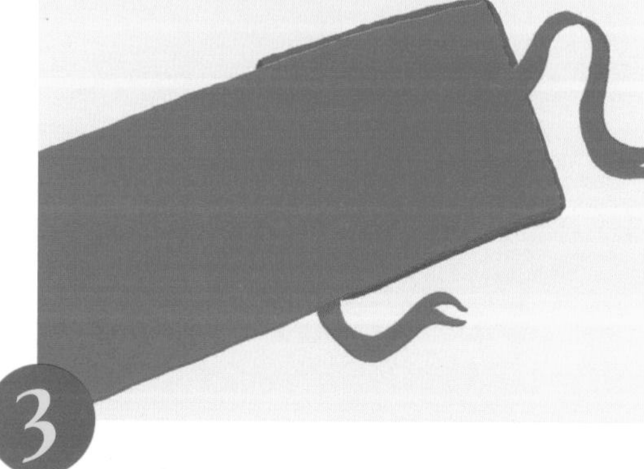

3 Glue the end of the sheet of turquoise paper to the wrong side of one of the purple boards.

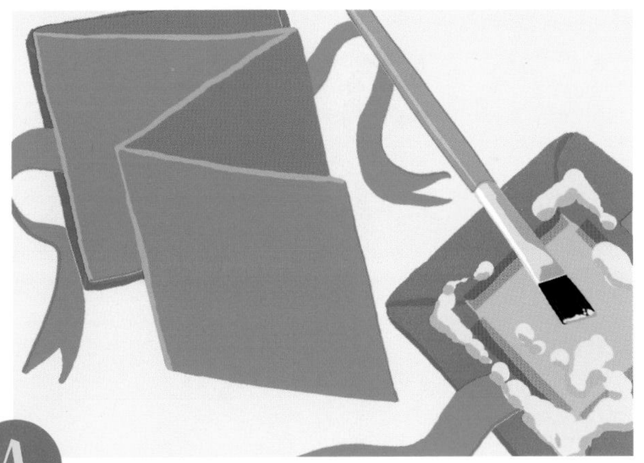

4

Fold the turquoise paper strip three times, concertina-style. Glue the last fold to the wrong side of the remaining purple board.

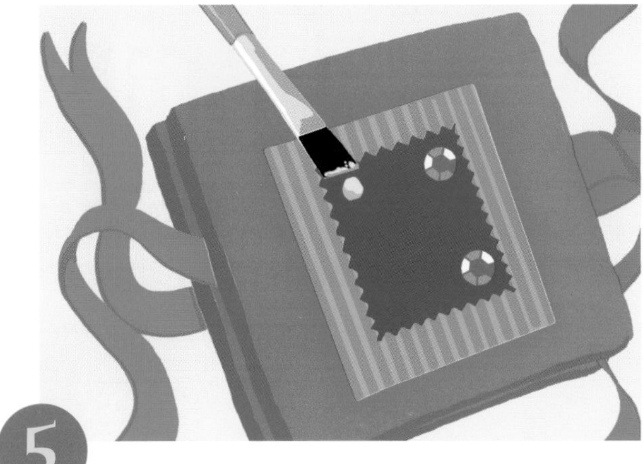

5

Decorate the front by sticking on some blue corrugated card, then a smaller square of purple felt cut with zig-zag scissors. Glue some gems to the felt as a finishing touch.

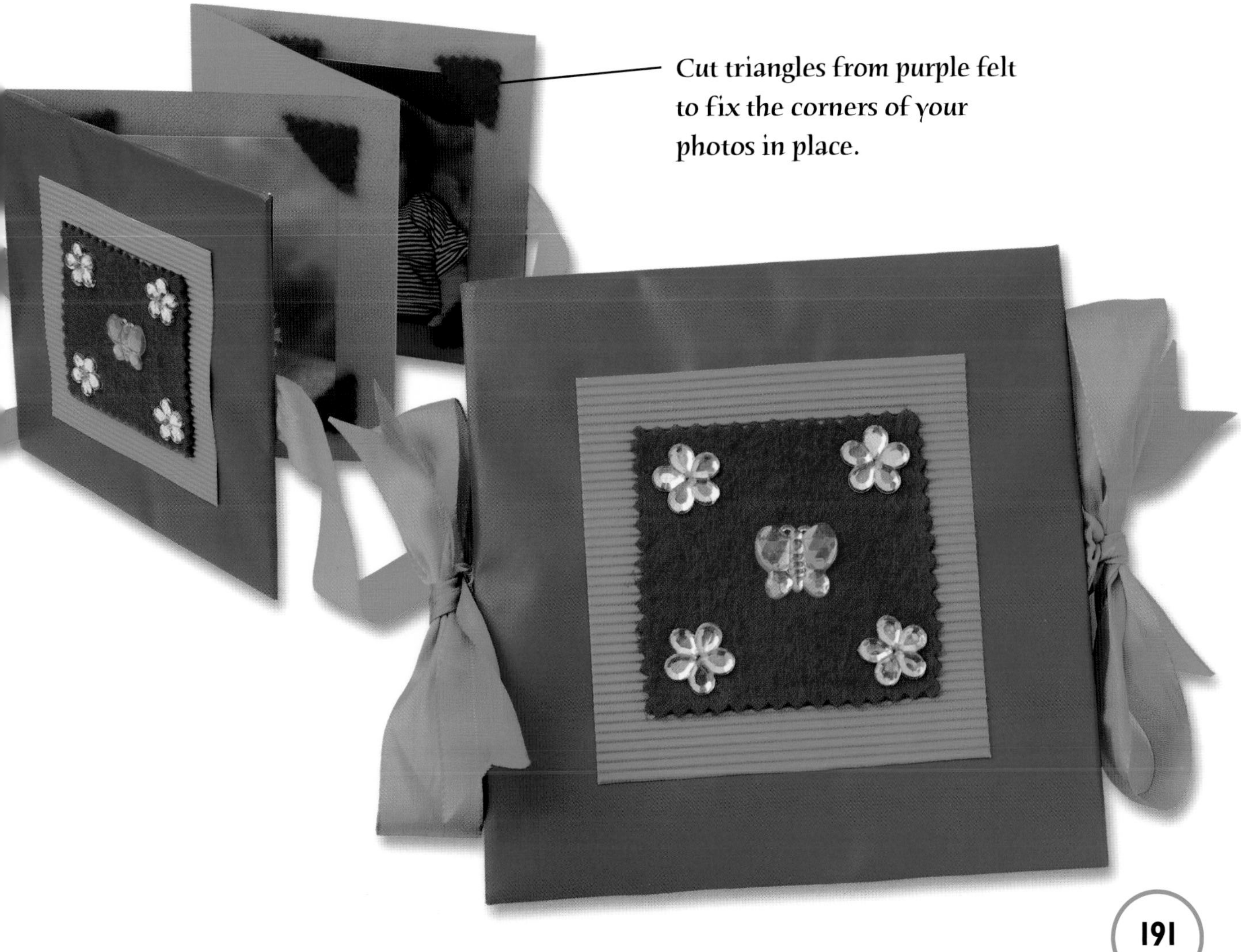

Cut triangles from purple felt to fix the corners of your photos in place.

Christmas stars

Are you looking forward to your next Christmas? Make some sparkly foil tree decorations while you wait for the big day.

You Will Need

- Thick card (eg. soap powder box)
- Tracing paper and pencil
- Scissors
- PVA glue
- Foil sweet wrappers
- Sequin stars
- Hole punch
- Gold cord

1 Trace the star from the template on p220. Put the tracing on the card and draw over the lines to transfer it to the card.

2 Use the scissors to cut out the star design.

3

Tear the sweet wrappers into small random pieces. Glue the pieces all over the star, overlapping them until the whole shape is covered. Leave to dry.

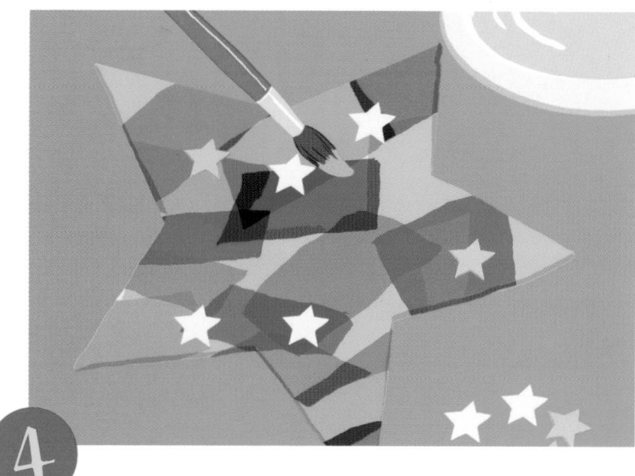

4

Glue sequin stars onto both sides of the foil-covered star. Leave to dry.

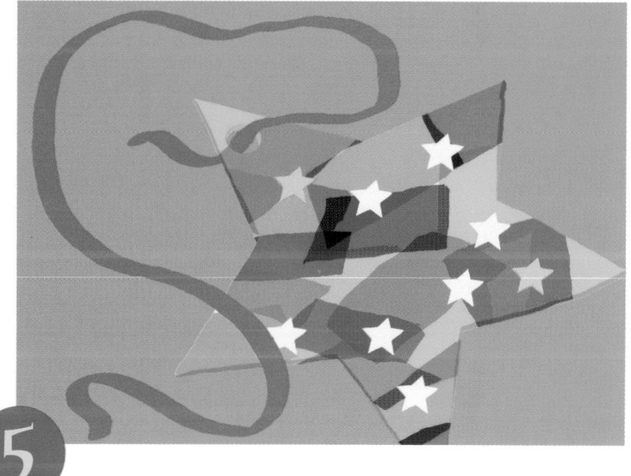

5

Use the hole punch to make a hole in one of the points of the star. Thread a length of gold cord through the hole and knot the ends together.

Try This!

Bells and trees

Make decorations in different shapes with a Christmas theme. Try a green tree or a bell covered in a chocolate orange wrapper.

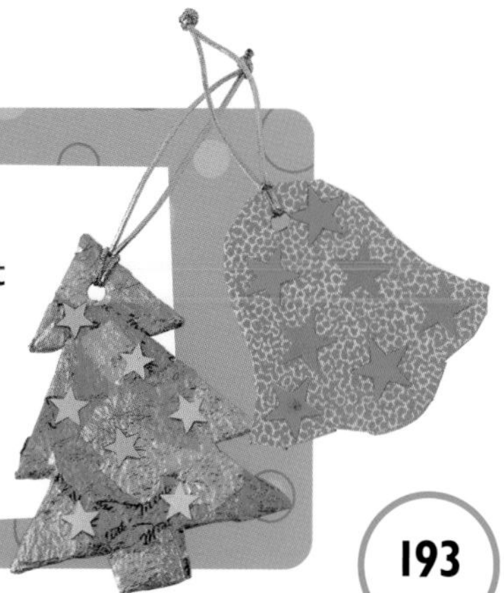

Halloween lantern

A glowing pumpkin lantern makes the perfect halloween decoration. Put one on your doorstep to greet trick-or-treaters.

You Will Need

- Medium-sized pumpkin
- Spoon or ice-cream scoop
- Felt-tipped pen
- Small knife
- Tea light

1 Scoop out the insides of the pumpkin, using a spoon or an ice cream scoop.

2 Use a felt-tipped pen to draw a scary face onto the pumpkin.

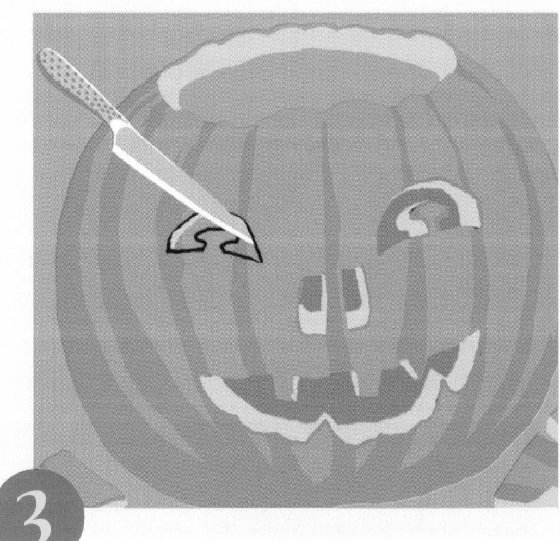

3 Now for the tricky part! Get an adult to cut away the marked pattern, using a small knife.

4

Put a tea light inside the pumpkin and get an adult to light it.

Try This!

Scary cat

You can make all kinds of faces on your pumpkin. This spooky witch's cat uses the stalk as a nose. Clever!

Top Tip

If your pumpkin dries out and looks withered, soak it in cold water for a few hours and it will be as good as new.

Nativity scene

This model looks beautiful and will help remind you of the wonderful story of the first ever Christmas.

You Will Need

- Packet of air-drying clay
- Acrylic paints: red, yellow, blue, green, black and gold

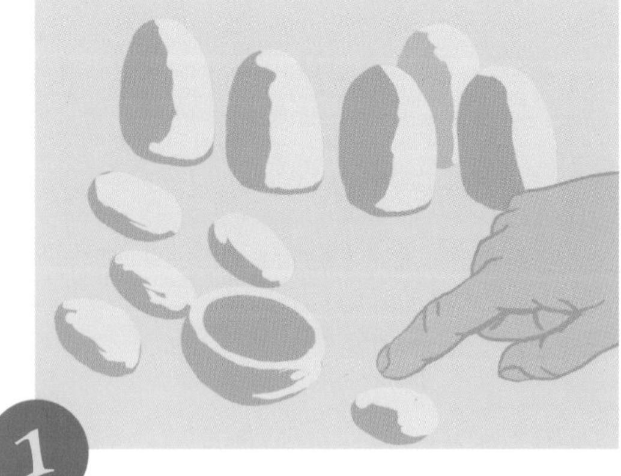

1

Make five thumb-shaped pieces of clay. These will be Mary, Joseph and three shepherds. Make four sheep-shaped lumps. Make a small ball and press it in the middle to make a cradle. Flatten a tiny ball to make a baby that will fit in the cradle. Leave them to dry.

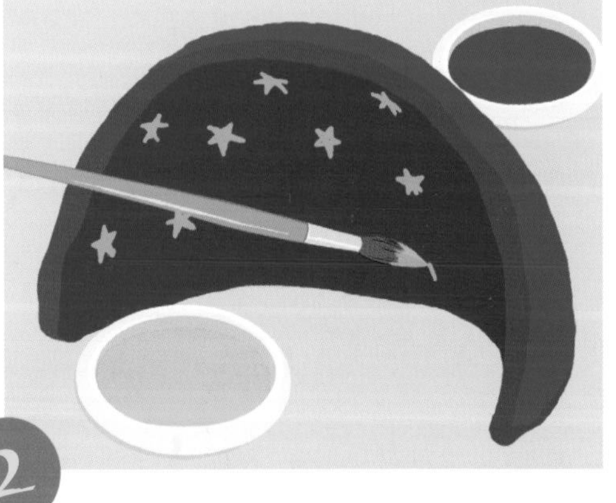

2

Roll out a fist-sized piece of clay and shape it onto a cave. When it is hard and dry, paint the cave dark blue, with tiny gold stars all over the inside.

3

Paint Mary and Joseph, using a small brush. Give Mary a blue veil and Joseph a green robe. Wait for the paint to dry before adding the details on the faces.

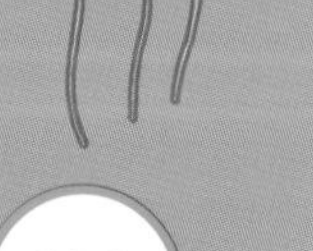

4

Paint the three shepherds with beards and headdresses. Paint the sheep white, with black faces and feet.

5

Paint the cradle. Make the baby white, with black stripes to show that he is wrapped in a sheet. When it is dry, paint the baby's face and features.

Three Kings

Add the three Kings to your Christmas scene. Paint gold details on their clothes to make them look grand.

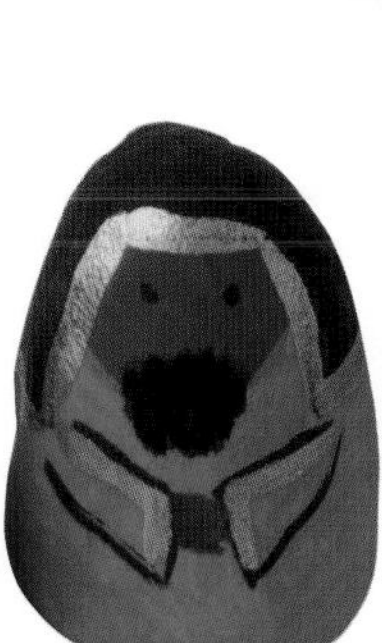

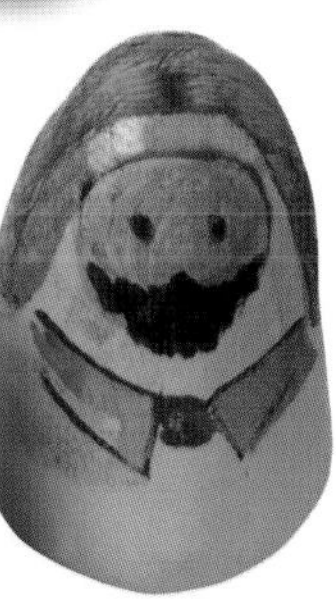

Golf paperweight

A golf-loving Dad will like this Fathers' Day gift. He might even give you extra pocket money!

You Will Need

- Wooden doorknob
- Paints: white, green, red
- Paintbrush
- Air-drying clay
- Strong wood glue

1 Paint the doorknob white and the flat top green. Put little tufts of grass round the bottom.

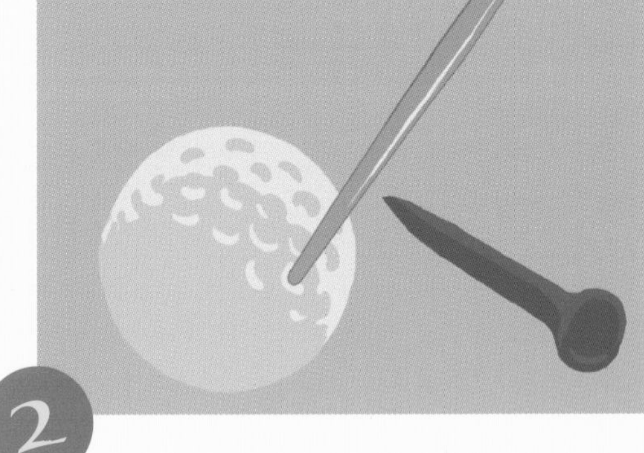

2 Roll a clay ball and make dimples with the end of the brush. Paint it white. Make a tee from the clay and paint it red.

3 When the clay has hardened, glue the ball and the tee to the green surface and leave it to dry.

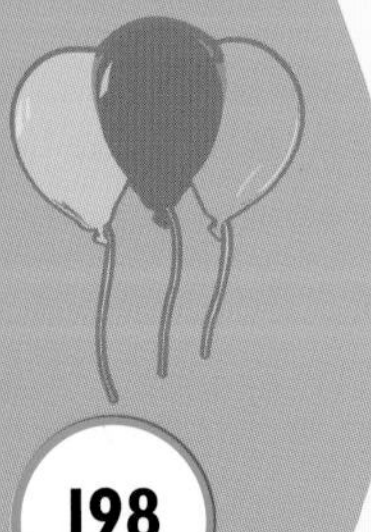

NATURECRAFT

Teasel mouse

A teasel is the dried head of a thistle. You can buy them in florists' or craft shops, and it's really simple to turn one into a cute little mouse.

1

Draw two mouse ear shapes. Colour them pink with brown rims and cut them out.

You Will Need

- ✦ Teasel with stem
- ✦ Coloured pencils: pink, brown
- ✦ Paper
- ✦ Glue
- ✦ 3 black map pins
- ✦ Piece of fabric 10 x 50cm
- ✦ Needle and thread
- ✦ Thin twig

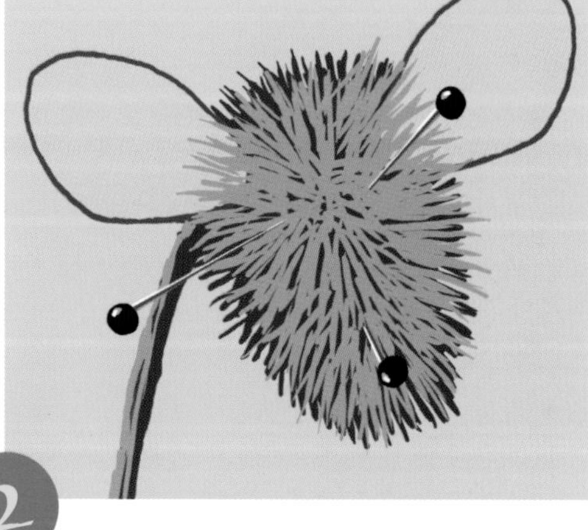

2

Push the ears into the teasel head and glue them in. Push in three pins, for eyes and a nose. Gently bend the teasel down a little so that it points forward on its stalk.

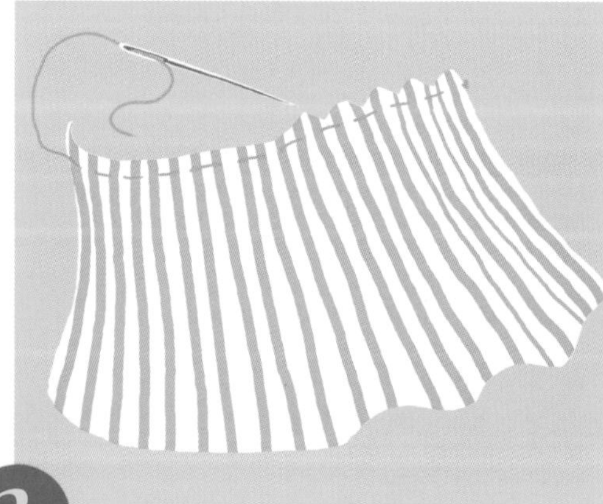

3

Make a dress by sewing a running stitch along one of the long edges of the fabric. Then pull the thread so that the fabric scrunches up. Cut the thread and knot the end.

4

Put the teasel inside the dress. Cut a small slit in each side of the dress and thread through a small twig to make arms.

Try This!

Pine cone owl

If you can't find a teasel, make Olly the owl instead, using a pine cone. Give him leaf wings and feet, stick-on card eyes, and glasses made from some fuse wire.

Shell jewellery box

Use seashells to make a luxury jewellery box from a humble cheese box. Collect shells if you live near the beach, or buy a bag from a craft shop.

You Will Need

- Round cheese box with lid
- 2 squares of red felt
- Pencil
- Scissors
- PVA glue and brush
- Blue acrylic paint and brush
- Assorted seashells

1 Draw round the lid of the box onto the red felt. Cut it out and stick it inside the lid. Repeat, and stick onto the base of the box.

2 Measure the depth of the box and cut a long strip of felt the same width. Glue it round the inside of the box, trimming the ends to make it fit neatly.

3 Paint the sides, the base and the outside of the lid in acrylic paint.

Try This!

Mini shell boxes

Tiny boxes can be decorated with a single shell. Use them as gift boxes for your home-made earrings and brooches.

4

Arrange the shells on the box lid and glue them on.

Twig furniture

You Will Need

- About 30 thin twigs
- Scissors
- Wood glue

Collect twigs from the garden or your local park and use them to make fun furniture – perhaps for a doll's house.

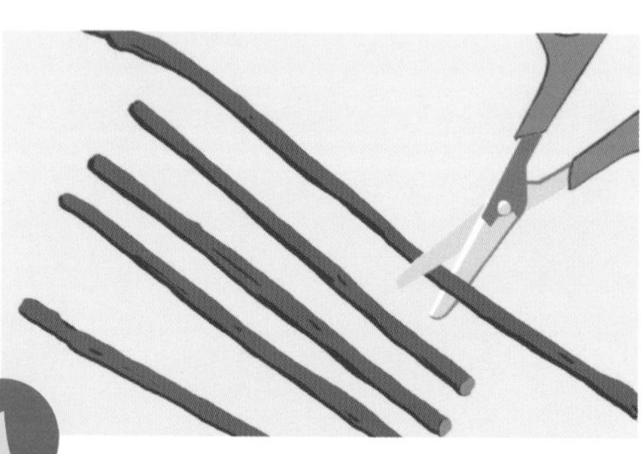

1 To make a chair, cut 15 thin sticks about 4cm long.

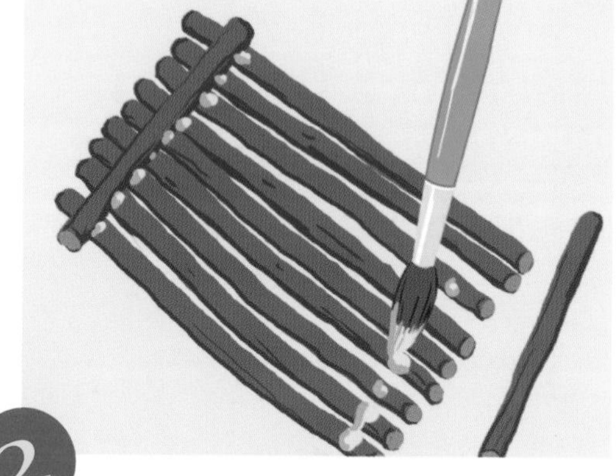

2 Put nine sticks side-by-side and glue two sticks at either end to hold them together.

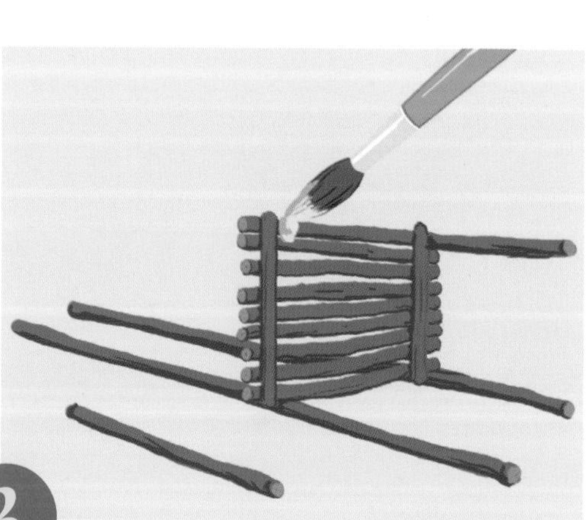

3 Cut two 12cm sticks for the back of the chair. Glue the seat halfway up the sticks. Glue two front legs, 6cms long, to the front of the seat.

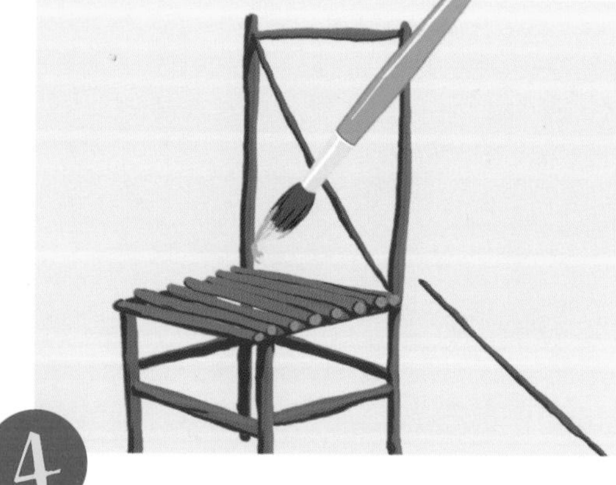

4 Glue four sticks round the bottom of the chair, and one at the top. Glue two sticks diagonally to the back to make a cross.

5

To make a table, glue eight sticks with a shorter stick at either end.

6

Glue four legs to the table top, then make the table sturdy by glueing two long and two short twigs to the legs, and two long twigs crosswise under the table.

Top Tip

To make little chair cushions, cut out a piece of fabric twice as long as the chair seat. Glue three edges, stuff it with cotton wool and glue the two edges together.

Cactus garden

You don't need to be an expert to grow a cactus garden. A sunny windowsill and some water once a week are all these prickly customers need.

You Will Need

- ✦ 5 small assorted cacti
- ✦ Bowl large enough for all 5 cacti
- ✦ Cactus compost
- ✦ Wad of kitchen paper
- ✦ Old spoon
- ✦ Coloured gravel

To move the cactus without pricking yourself on the spines, wrap a thick wad of kitchen paper round it.

1

Put a thin layer of gravel in the bottom of the bowl. Add a layer of compost to within 2cm of the top of the bowl. Use your finger to make a hole in the compost towards the back of the bowl.

2

Choose the tallest cactus and remove it from its pot. Put it in the hole you have made and use your fingers to push the compost down firmly all round it.

3

Make another hole in the compost and plant the next tallest cactus in the same way as before.

Top Tip

If you don't have coloured gravel, make a desert garden instead by spreading sand on top of the compost.

4

Continue planting. Use an old spoon to press the compost down firmly around the base of each cactus.

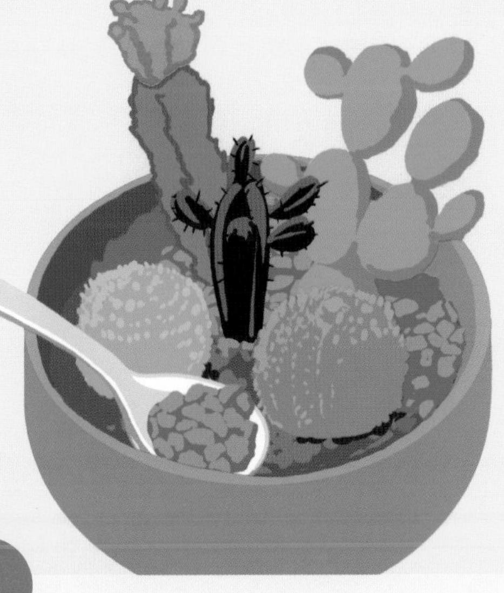

5

Using the spoon, arrange the gravel around the base of each cactus until the compost is covered.

Pebble hedgehog family

The best pebbles for painting are the smooth type you can find on the beach, so on your next seaside trip, keep a lookout for suitable ones.

You Will Need

- ✦ 1 large and 2 small smooth stones
- ✦ Acrylic paints: grey, black and white
- ✦ Paintbrushes: medium and small
- ✦ Clear varnish

1 Wash and dry the stones. Paint them grey all over and leave them to dry. Paint an extra coat if you need to.

2 Use the fine paintbrush to paint black bristles all over the tops of the pebbles.

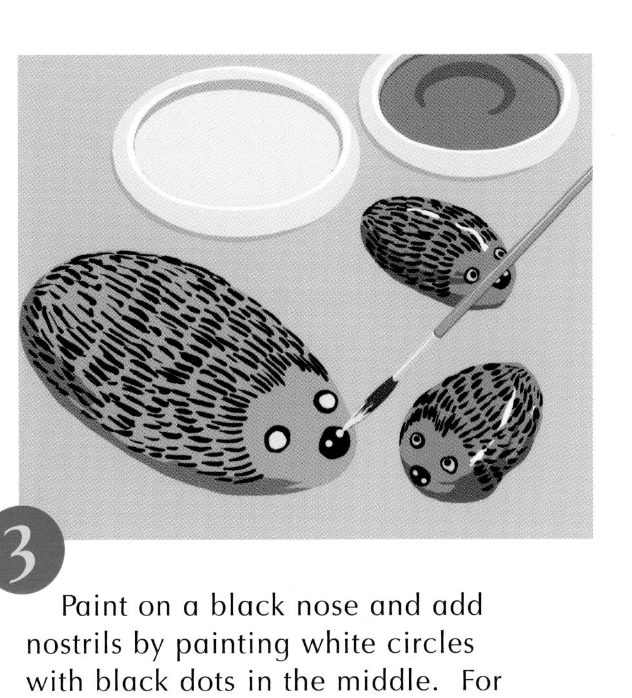

3

Paint on a black nose and add nostrils by painting white circles with black dots in the middle. For eyes, make two black circles, smaller white circles inside and black dots in the middle. Now paint the baby hedgehogs in the same way.

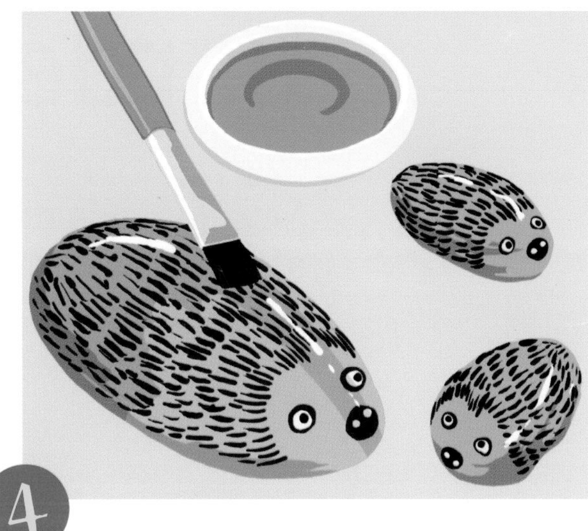

4

If the hedgehogs are going to live on the doorstep or in the garden, give them all a coat of clear varnish.

Try This!

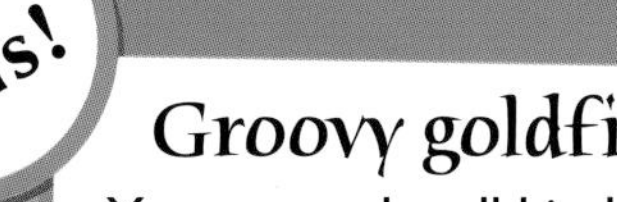

Groovy goldfish

You can make all kinds of pebble creatures – look at the shape of the pebble and see what it reminds you of. This one has been turned into a scaly goldfish.

NATURECRAFT

Garden on a plate

Making a miniature garden is a fun activity on a rainy day. Collect tiny cuttings of shrubs and flowers from the garden and get busy!

1

Put a 2cm layer of compost on the plate. Press moss into about ¾ of the area.

You Will Need

- ✦ Old dinner plate
- ✦ Potting compost
- ✦ Moss, grass and small flowers, eg. daisies
- ✦ Cuttings from shrubs
- ✦ Fir tree twig
- ✦ Kitchen foil
- ✦ Jam jar lid
- ✦ 2 twigs and string
- ✦ Paper and coloured pencils
- ✦ Scissors

2

Put small pebbles round the plate edge and make a path of pebbles in the soil, as shown.

3

Push a fir twig into the soil to make a miniature tree. Push the flowers, shrubs and grass into the soil.

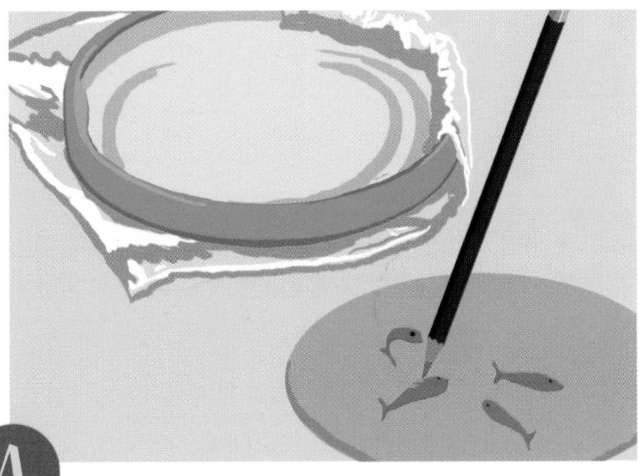

4

Mould kitchen foil round a jam jar lid to make a pond. Cut out a circle to fit in the bottom of the pond. Colour it blue and draw some goldfish onto it. Put some more blades of grass round the pond to look like reeds.

5

Draw some clothes on a piece of white paper, giving them tags so you can hang them on a washing line. Colour them and cut them out.

Top Tip

Spray your garden with water to keep it fresh. Replace the flowers when they begin to wilt.

6

Make a washing line from twigs and string. Hide two blobs of plasticine in the moss and push the twigs into them. Glue the clothes to the line.

NATURECRAFT

Pressed flower card

Pressed flowers are brilliant for making cards, but don't forget to check with an adult before you pick the petals off their favourite flowers!

You Will Need

- ✦ Flowers and leaves
- ✦ Heavy books
- ✦ Kitchen paper
- ✦ PVA glue mixed with equal amount of water
- ✦ Cream card 40 x 20cm

1

◄ Pick some flower petals and leaves. Arrange them on kitchen paper, then put another piece of paper on top. Put them inside a book.

2

◂ Place a pile of heavy books on top of the book with the flowers inside. Leave them for at least two weeks.

3

Fold the cream card in half and make a sharp crease with the outside of the scissors and a ruler.

4

Remove the pressed flowers from the book. Arrange them on the front of the card and glue the petals and leaves into position.

NATURECRAFT

Bottle garden

If you'd like a garden but you don't fancy the idea of all that weeding and mowing the lawn, this bottle garden is perfect. Just remember to water it once a week and your plants will be happy.

You Will Need

- ✦ Large glass jar with lid
- ✦ Sticky tape
- ✦ Old spoon
- ✦ Cotton wool ball
- ✦ 2 kebab sticks
- ✦ Coloured gravel
- ✦ Potting compost
- ✦ Small plants

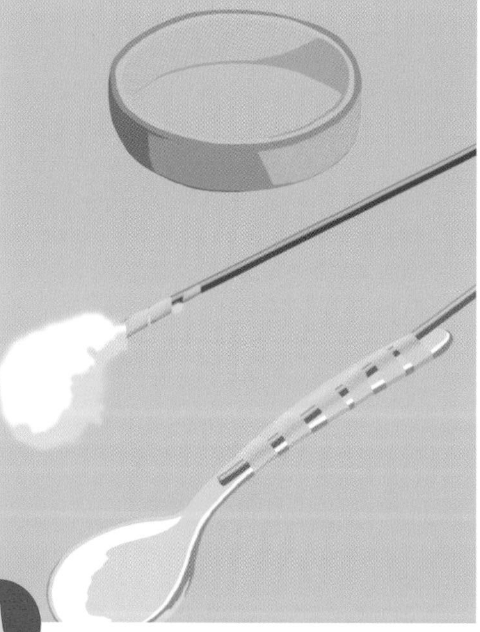

1 Start by making tools. Make a digger by taping a spoon to a kebab stick, using lots of sticky tape. Make a cleaning tool by taping a ball of cotton wool to the other stick.

2 Spoon about 4cm of coloured gravel into the bottom of the jar.

3

Now add about 8cm of moist compost and press it down with your hands.

4

Use the spoon and your hands to make a hole and put a small plant in it. Press down firmly round the base, then put in two or three more plants.

5

Dip the cotton wool in water and squeeze it out. Use your cleaning tool to wipe away any smears of compost from the sides of the jar.

Make your bottle garden more interesting with a tropical bird on a stick. Look for these in garden centres.

Leaf puppet

Here's a bright idea for an autumn day. Why not collect some interesting leaves and make a puppet, complete with leafy outfit?

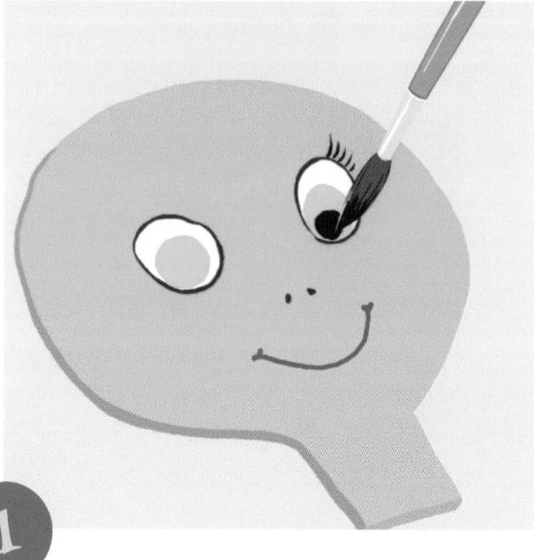

1

Draw a face and neck about 4cm long. Colour in the face and give her eyes, nose and a mouth but no hair! Cut the shape out.

You Will Need

- White paper
- Set of paints or pencils
- Scissors
- PVA glue
- Autumn leaves
- Sequins
- Glitter
- Twigs: 2 x 10cm, 1 x 20cm
- Sticky tape

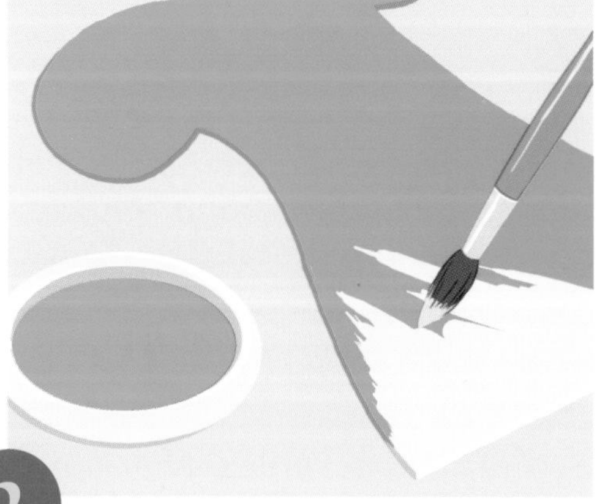

2

Draw, colour in and cut out a dress shape, about 15cm long. Glue the head to the dress.

3

Glue small pointed leaves round the face to make hair. Glue leaves onto the dress, starting with large leaves at the bottom, and using smaller ones nearer the waist.

4

◂ Glue sequins to the neck, sleeves and waist of the dress, then dot some over the leaves. Brush a little glue on the leaf edges, then sprinkle glitter over them. Leave to dry.

5

Turn the figure over and stick a small twig to each sleeve with tape. Tape a long twig up the length of the puppet, leaving about 10cm at the bottom.

NATURECRAFT

Sand butterfly

Did you know you can paint with sand? It sounds mad, but you can make brilliant textured pictures. Buy sets of coloured sand in craft shops.

You Will Need

- ✦ A4 sheet of blue card
- ✦ A4 sheet of white paper and pencil
- ✦ Scissors
- ✦ Black felt-tipped pen
- ✦ A3 sheet scrap paper
- ✦ PVA glue and stiff brush
- ✦ Coloured sand: red, orange, yellow ochre, blue, green
- ✦ Teaspoon

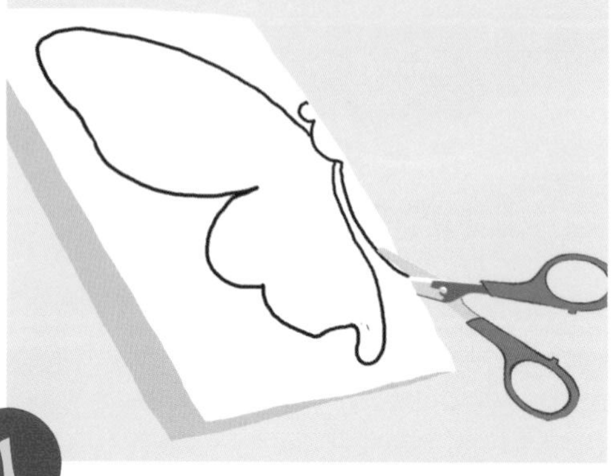

1

Fold the white paper in half and draw half a butterfly's body and a wing. Cut it out. Unfold the shape and put it on the sheet of blue card at an angle.

2

Use the black felt-tipped pen to draw round the outline, then put on markings, matching the pattern on each wing.

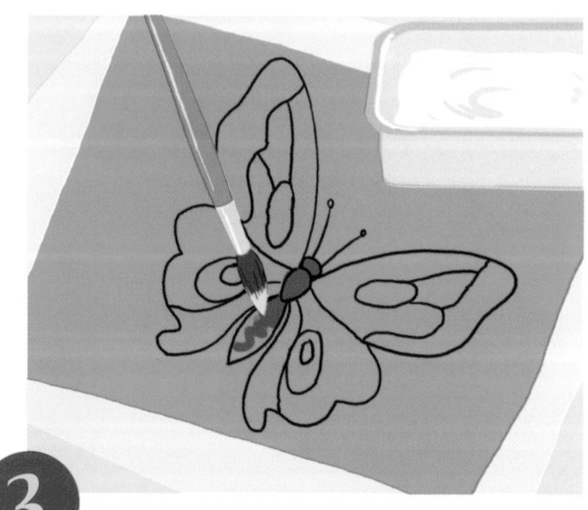

3

Place the scrap paper under the card. Paste a thin layer of PVA glue over the butterfly's body and head only.

4

Pour some yellow ochre sand into the spoon and sprinkle over the glued area. Lift the picture with both hands and gently tap the spare sand onto the scrap paper. Tip the sand carefully back into its container.

5

Continue glueing and sprinkling, working on a small area at a time so that the glue does not dry out before you add the sand.

Try This!

Dragonfly

This shimmering dragonfly is made in the same way as the butterfly. The white background makes the colourful sand stand out brilliantly.

Top templates

Draw round these shapes with a pencil onto tracing paper, then turn the tracing paper over lay on plain paper and scribble over the lines.

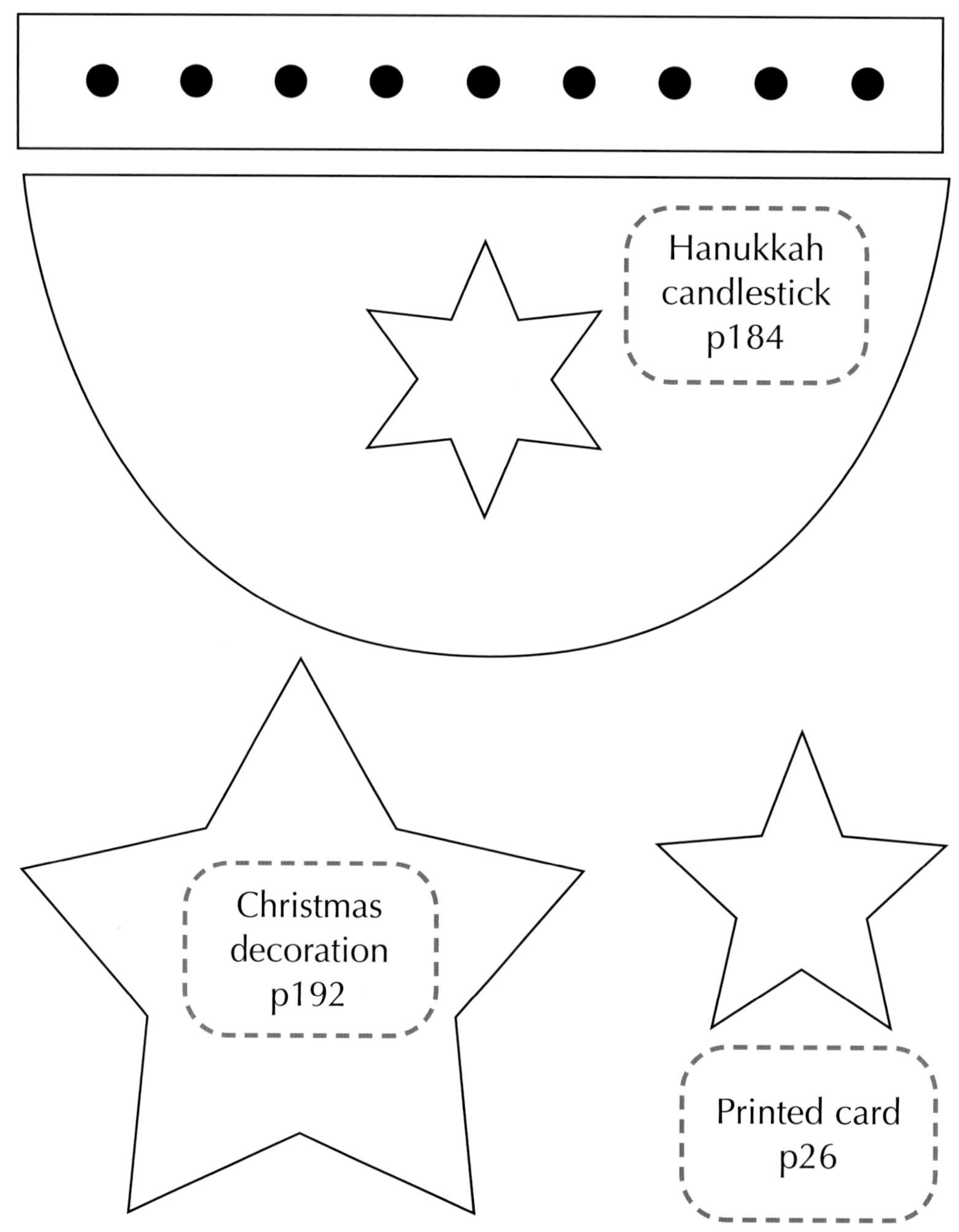

Halloween bat
card
p180
Dinosaur
letter rack
p16

Royal crown
p164

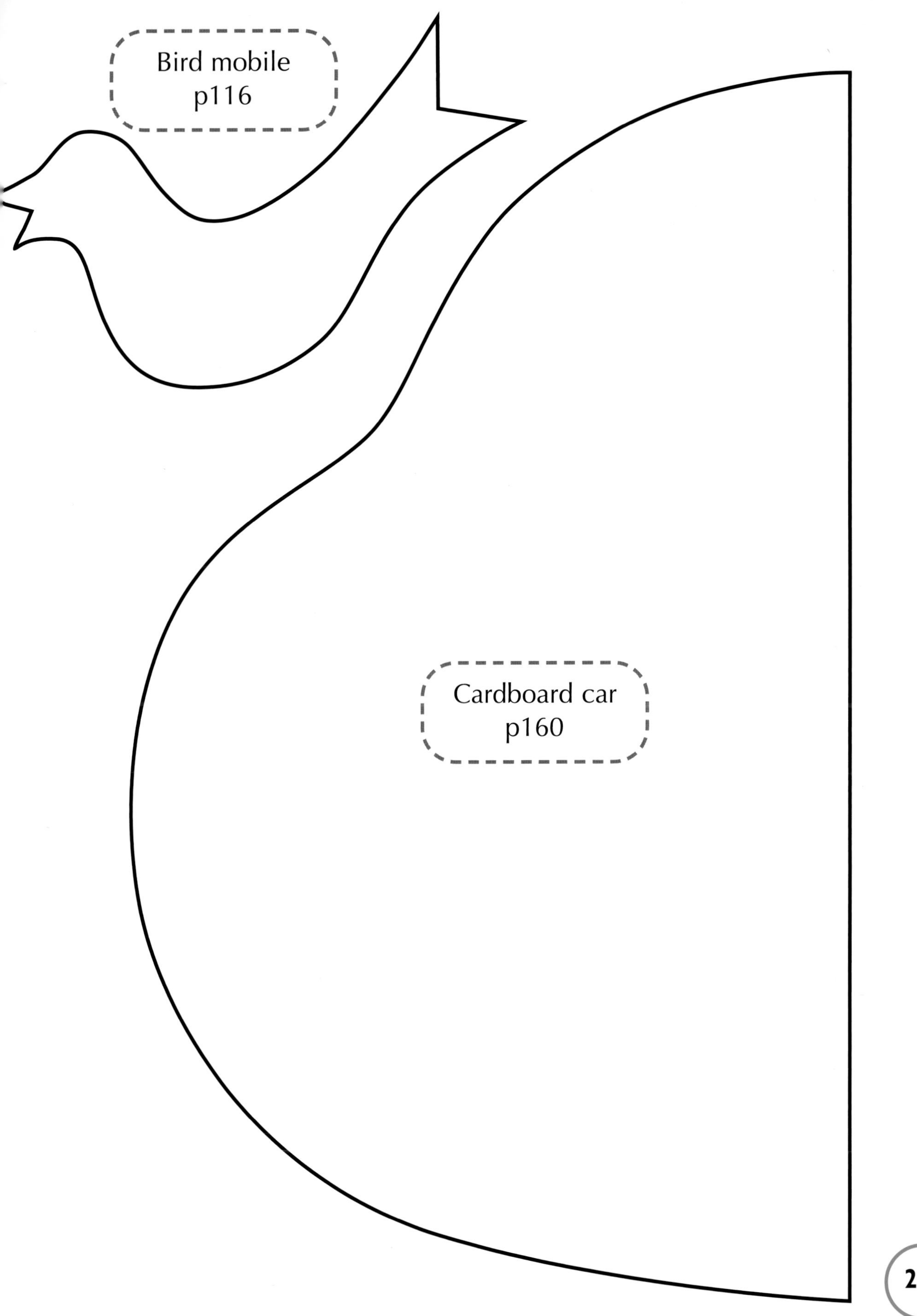
Bird mobile
p116
Cardboard car
p160

Index

Credits

Project creators: Anita Ruddell
Melanie Williams
Illustrator: Gary Walton

Photographer: John Englefield
Project editor: Rona Skene
Produced by DropCap Ltd